HIS FIRST 40 YEARS

Dennis the Menace

HIS FIRST 40 YEARS

Hank Ketcham

ABBEVILLE PRESS · PUBLISHERS

NEW YORK · LONDON · PARIS

Editor: Walton Rawls
Designer: Molly Shields
Copy Chief: Robin James
Production Supervisor: Hope Koturo

Library of Congress Cataloging-in-Publication
Data
Ketcham, Hank, 1920–
    Dennis the Menace—his first 40 years / Hank
Ketcham.
        p.   cm.
    ISBN 1-55859-157-5
    1. American wit and humor, Pictorial.   2. Cari-
catures and cartoons—United States—History—
20th century.   I. Title.
NC1429.K52A4   1991
741.5′973—dc20   90-23973
                                                                CIP

As Dennis explained it to his short friend Joey: "My dad tells it the way it *is*, but Mr. Wilson tells it the way it *was*." In the tradition of Edward R. Murrow, Walter Cronkite, and George Wilson, this book *is* THE WAY IT WAS.

Free-lance cartooning had proved to be easy, fun, and most profitable for me, but I still yearned to have a syndicated newspaper feature. Instead of selling a drawing to one client for one fee, it seemed more appealing to sell its reproduction rights to hundreds of newspapers at a single clip. Even though each paper would contribute only a modest sum, the aggregate could prove to be substantial, and I wouldn't be risking all my goodies in one basket.

In June of 1950, I was part of a group from the National Cartoonists Society attending the annual Newspaper Publishers Convention, and I took the opportunity to find out more about the mysterious business of newspaper syndication. Allen Saunders, the talented writer behind "Mary Worth," "Kerry Drake," and other huge successes was there and kind enough to act as my mentor. He was familiar with my magazine work and gave generously of his time to explain the technical details with encouragement. However, Allen clearly stressed "two important traps to avoid":

1. Do not submit a single-panel feature to a syndicate. It is too easy for an editor to drop it, and generally panels don't bring the fees enjoyed by the strips.

2. Under no circumstances even consider featuring the antics of a small child; this kind of humor is already a glut on the postwar market.

The following March, *Dennis the Menace* was first released and began to appear in papers all over the country. In August, I ran into Ted Durein, the feature editor of my local *Monterey Peninsula Herald*, where *Dennis* had only begun to run the week before.

"I'm relieved you finally found a place for this home-town boy in your comics section, Ted. It sure took you a long time," I grumped, "to make up your mind."

"Y'know, Hank," he laughed, "space is always the problem. We had to decide which cartoonist to drop to make room for you, and that's always a tough decision."

I wasn't yet too familiar with that side of the business, but, at any rate, I felt better that my neighbors and creditors could see that I had a steady job.

"How does it look to you?" I asked cautiously.

"It's rather funny," he said. "Yeah, I like it. But I don't see how it can last more than a year or two. I mean, after all . . . there's only so much you can say about a five-year-old kid!" *He might be right.*

Hank Ketcham

THE 1950s

"*HOW* DID CURIOSITY KILL THE CAT? AND WHICH CAT WAS IT? AND WHO'S CURIOSITY?"

Maybe *YOU'VE* NEVER BEEN INSIDE A BOTTLE OF INDIA INK, BUT TAKE IT FROM ME, THERE'S NOT MUCH OF A VIEW. SO, I WAS GREATLY RELIEVED, BACK IN THE FALL OF 1950, TO BE DRAWN INTO THE REAL WORLD ON THE TIP OF A TINY COPPER PENPOINT — WHEN HANK PUT ME TO WORK ON WHAT HE HOPED MIGHT TURN OUT TO BE A STEADY JOB...FOR *HIM*.

I GUESS I WAS A STRANGE-LOOKING KID IN THOSE DAYS. AND HANK HAD ME DOING SOME PRETTY WILD STUFF...NO WONDER I HAD TO SIT IN THE CORNER SO OFTEN. BUT I WAS HAVING A WHOLE LOT OF FUN, AND HE TOLD ME THAT PEOPLE WERE LAUGHING THEIR HEADS OFF. IT SURE BEAT THE PANTS OFF STAYING INSIDE THAT INK BOTTLE.

"WHAT'S SO FUNNY? DIDN'T THE FARMER'S DAUGHTER WANT A BATH BRUSH?"

DISCIPLINE

"DON'T YOU SHUSH ME, YOUNG MAN! THIS IS MY POND AND MY FISH, AND I'LL TALK AS LOUD AS I PLEASE!"

"EVER SEE SO MUCH JUNK IN ALL YOUR LIFE?"

"BE SURE AND WRITE TO US WHEN YOU LEARN HOW."

"MY DAD GOT A BUNCH OF BRAND-NEW DIMES 'SPECIALLY FOR THIS TRIP."

"HE ISN'T FEELING GOOD. I'M GIVING HIM HIS BREAKFAST IN BED."

"NOW TAKE IT A LITTLE EASY. MY DADDY IS 30 YEARS OLD!"

"WHY DO I HAVE TO DRESS UP TO COME HERE? WHO AM I TRYIN' TO *KID*?"

"HOW MUCH DID YOU GET, DAD?"

"GEE, IT SEEMS FUNNY TO SAY YOUR PRAYERS WITH ALL YOUR CLOTHES ON!"

"I THOUGHT I'D PASS IT AROUND IN CHURCH."

"HOW CAN I GET TO HEAVEN IF I DON'T GET MY WINGS 'TIL I *GET* THERE?"

"BLACK'S YOUR FAVORITE COLOR, ISN'T IT?"

"NEXT TIME WOULD YA ASK THE GUY TO PLAY A FEW COWBOY SONGS?"

"SHE MUSTA CHANGED HER MIND. SHE WENT DOWN THE AISLE WITH AN OLDER GUY."

THE 1950s

"I SAID, IF YOU WANT MY BUSINESS, YOU'RE GONNA HAVE TO PUT IN LOWER WINDOWS!"

"FIRST, TELL ME WHAT YOU'VE FOUND."

"I THOUGHT I'D BETTER CHECK, MRS. MITCHELL. YOUR NOTE SAID 'NO MILK', BUT IT'S WRITTEN IN CRAYON AND MILK IS SPELT M-E-L-K."

"OKAY IF I GET MY BASEBALL OUTA YOUR CAN OF PAINT, MISTER?"

"GET YOUR RED HOTS! ..I **DID** PUT MUSTARD ON IT ... GET YOUR RED...BEAT IT, KID! ... GET YOUR ... *LISTEN*, KID! ..."

"GOD BLESS MOM 'N' DAD AND THE GUY THAT FIXES OUR TV..."

"MR. TAYLOR, DO WE NEED ANY PAN-LICKERS?"

"I'M SORRY, BUT THAT'S THE WAY IT IS . . . . . UP OR DOWN."

"Pssst! I know where she hid your glasses!"

"She's sure got a crazy 'frigerator! It's just got one GREAT BIG ice cube in it!"

"I don't see no blue streak when she talks!"

"Get your GAS-MASK, MOM! This guy smokes a pipe, too!"

"IF WHAT I SAID WASN'T FUNNY, WHY IS EVERYBODY TRYIN' NOT TO LAUGH?"

"WHATTA YA MEAN 'BEFORE WE HAD A TELEBISHION SET'? WE'VE *ALWAYS* HAD A TELEBISHION SET!"

"MAYBE I'D BETTER SEE IF DAD'S GETTING ENOUGH AIR IN THAT CLOSET."

"WHERE DO YOU KEEP YOUR BELFRY, MR. WEDGE? I'D LIKE TO SEE YOUR BATS!"

THE 1950s

"WHAT ARE YOU *WAITIN'* FOR, DAD? *AFRAID?*"

"I TOLD YOU *NOT* TO OPEN THE DOOR, DIDN'T I? WELL, DIDN'T I?"

"THAT'S WHAT I LIKE ABOUT SPEAR-FISHIN'. AT LEAST YA *SEE* SOME FISH!"

"ANOTHER SWELL GAME WE HAVEN'T PLAYED IN A LONG TIME IS LOCKING OURSELVES IN THE CAR AND BLOWING THE HORN."

"PASS IT ON, KID! HEY, KID! THAT'S *MY* HOTDOG!
HEY, KID.....!"

"IN CASE YOU DON'T GET TO HEAR IT, MOM, IT GOES 'PUT-PUT-PUT-PUT'."

"ANYWAY, I'LL BET THEY FLY HIGHER FROM NOW ON!"

THE 1950s

"YEP, THAT SOUNDED LIKE A MOUNTAIN LION ALL RIGHT.
SURE WISH I HAD A NICE HOME TO SLEEP IN TONIGHT."

"WHO NEEDS A SALAD?"

"WELL, NOW WE KNOW WHAT MADE IT SO NICE 'N' SOFT."

"WANT SOME OF THIS TO THROW? IT'S RICE PUDDING."

"NOW DON'T GET EXCITED! I'M JUST GONNA GIVE 'EM A GOOD MEAL AND SEND 'EM ON THEIR WAY!"

"WAIT A SEC! I WANT SOMETHIN' BACK!"

"HEY, WAKE UP 'N SEE HOW YOU LOOK WITH A CREW HAIRCUT!"

"GETS UP LATE, DON'T HE?"

"YOU HAVE A COLLECT CALL FROM WHOM? DENNIS WHO?"

"HE'S SUCH AN AFFECTIONATE KID. WHY DO FOLKS CALL HIM DENNIS THE MENACE?"

"HER NAME? WELL, IT'S..UH...IT'S BESSIE. YEAH. BESSIE IS YOUR COW, DENNIS."

"CATCH, DAD!"

"...'WASH YOUR HANDS! DRINK YOUR MILK! TAKE YOUR NAP!' DON'T YOU SEE WHAT SHE'S DOIN'? SHE'S BOSSIN' US!"

"WHO'S PETER? AND WHY'RE YOU GONNA ROB HIM AND PAY PAUL? AND WHO'S PAUL?"

"MOM SAYS DAD CAN'T BUY ONE UNTIL WE GET THE ELECTRIC TOASTER PAID FOR!"

"LOOK WHAT I FOUND! A *FULL LENGTH* MIRROR!"

"I'VE BEEN SITTIN' UP HERE THINKIN' ABOUT THE GOOD OLD DAYS!"

THE 1950s

"LEAVE IT ALONE!"

"I'VE BEEN THROUGH TWO WARS, DEPRESSION, AUTO ACCIDENT, FLOOD, MARRIAGE, *EVERYTHING*, SEE? BUT A FEW YEARS AGO WE MOVED NEXT DOOR TO A LITTLE KID....."

" 'BOUT A MILLION KEEN LITTLE CARS TO RIDE IN, AN' I HAVE TO BE WITH SOMEBODY THAT LIKES TO *WALK*!"

"IT DOESN'T LOOK UNBREAKABLE TO ME!"

"MOM, HOW'D YOU LIKE TO FINISH MAKING SOME WAFFLES?"

"THEY GOT ANY *HORSES* AT THE POOR FARM?"

"PIGEONS GOTTA DRINK *TOO*, YA KNOW!"

THE 1950s

"DADDY ALWAYS SAYS NO AT FIRST, BUT IF YOU KEEP ASKIN' AND WHINE A LITTLE BIT, SOMETIMES HE CHANGES HIS MIND."

"BETTER GET A *BIG* BOOK! IT'S RAININ' CATS 'N' DOGS!"

"I DON'T NEED TO RELAX, DOCTOR! *HE* NEEDS TO RELAX!"

"BRING YOUR CAMERA, DAD! HERE'S SOME *REAL* CHARACTERS!"

"CAN I USE HIM NEXT?"

"WAVE AT THE KID, CHARLIE. HE THROWS A LOT OF BUSINESS OUR WAY."

"YOU SURE GOT A NICE SEWER DOWN HERE!"

"LOOK AT ALL THE PRETTY THINGS MR. WILSON PLANTED IN HIS GARDEN!"

THE 1950s

"WHAT DO YOU MEAN HE'S SQUIRTING YOU WITH A GARDEN HOSE? HE'S UP IN HIS ROOM!"

"I MUST BE GROWIN'! DID YA NOTICE HE KEPT CALLIN' ME 'MAN'?"

"I GOT FOUR. HOW MANY BOX TOPS DO WE NEED?"

"I COULD PAY A PENNY NOW AN' A FEW PENNIES A WEEK...?"

"I'M GONNA GIVE THE CANARY A BATH. WHY?"

"IT'S SURE NICE TO HAVE SOMEBODY TO TALK TO, GRANDPA. MOM 'N DAD GET *SORE* IF I WAKE *THEM* UP!"

"WELL, THERE'S *ANOTHER* YARD I'D BETTER STAY OUT OF IF I KNOW WHAT'S GOOD FOR ME!"

"GET HIM OUT OF HERE, NURSE! I'M NOT WELL."

THE 1950s

"ANYTHING YOU WANT ME TO ASK HIM FOR YOU?"

"I'M GOIN' OVER TO THE WILSONS. I GOTTA GET SOME SLEEP!"

"YOU'RE NOT AFRAID OF A LITTLE THUNDER, ARE YOU?"

"HERE. ALL I WANTED WAS A SIP."

"GEE, YOU ACT LIKE YOU NEVER *FELT* AN ICICLE BEFORE."

"...WELL, IF HE'S BEEN SO BAD, WHY DIDN'T YOU CALL EARLIER? *WHAT?* WELL, HOW DID YOU GET *UNTIED* ?....."

"GEE, THAT COW MUSTA BEEN *SOME* JUMPER!"

"MAD, ISN'T SHE?"

"MARGARET IS CRAZY! I DON'T SEE NO **BLACK ROOTS!**"

"LISTEN, ALICE, HE'S JUST FAKING BECAUSE HE KNOWS YOU'LL JUMP ON ME! ALICE, LISTEN A MINUTE . . ."

"WHO ARE YOU CALLING A CRAZY MIXED-UP BLOND?"

"HOW COME *MY* FOOD IS ALWAYS SO DARN SLIPPERY?"

"WHY DID YOU LAUGH WHEN SHE CALLED ME A LITTLE GENTLEMAN?"

"HI, MOM! IS THAT DAD?"

"YOU LADIES GO RIGHT AHEAD. I'M LOOKING FOR MY DAD."

"COME AND GET IT!"

"THE MITCHELLS AREN'T HOME. WOULD YOU LIKE TO SPEAK TO THE REASON WHY THEY AREN'T?"

"I GOT A BIG RANCH IN TEXAS! WITH SIXTEEN MILLION COWS 'N HORSES! AN' TWO WHITE RATS."

"SEE? THEY DON'T MAKE THE HORSE THAT I CAN'T RIDE!"

"GIRLS! ALWAYS DRESSIN' UP AN' TRYIN' TO PRETEND THEY'RE BIG."

"SOLD! TO THE MAN HOLDING HIS HAND OVER HIS LITTLE BOY'S MOUTH!"

"HANG ON TIGHT, LADY! I'M TAKIN' THIS STAGECOACH TO TEXAS!"

"YOU PASSED AWFULLY CLOSE TO THAT POLICEMAN BACK THERE."

"STRUT, YOU BIG BULLY!"

"YOU BOTH KNOW THE RULES: STAY OUT OF THE REFRIGERATOR, NO HITTING WITH THE CLOSED FIST, AND PROTECT YOURSELF AT ALL TIMES."

"SEE? SEE HOW FLAT THEY ARE?"

"COME AND *GET* ME!"

"YOU DIDN'T *CATCH* US! WE RAN *OUTA GAS!*"

"THAT'S PRETTY GRUESOME. BUT LET ME TELL YOU WHAT HE DID TO *ME* ONE NIGHT WHEN I WAS SITTING WITH HIM..."

"THE SITTER SAYS EVERYTHING IS *PEACEFUL.* DENNIS LEFT THE HOUSE RIGHT AFTER WE DID."

"DON'T PULL, DENNIS. JUST *HANG ON!*"

"WHEN I WAS A KID WE WOULDN'T FOOL WITH ONE THAT SMALL."

'LOOK AROUND, YOUNG MAN. I'M SUPPOSED TO HAVE ANOTHER BANANA!'

"I DON'T THINK IT'S ROMANTIC. I THINK IT'S DARK!"

"NOW DON'T GET SORE, HENRY. MAYBE HE'S JUST LUCKY."

"THERE! NOW YOU CAN TAKE YOUR BATH....BUT YOU WON'T HAVE ANY FUN!"

"CATCH, DAD! CORN FLAKES!"

"COME OUT OF THERE, DENNIS! HE WASN'T HOLDING THAT DOOR OPEN FOR YOU!"

THE 1950s

"DON'T *RUSH* ME. LET'S SEE, THERE'S DANCER AND PRANCER AND...AND..."

"HI, MRS. WILSON! THIS SURE IS HOT CHOCOLATE WEATHER, ISN'T IT?"

"DENNIS!"

"DOES HAVIN' THE FLU MEAN HE CAN'T TEACH ME TO ICE SKATE THIS AFTERNOON?"

"MY DAD SAYS HE THINKS IT'S BETTER TO GIVE THAN TO GET. LUCKY FOR ME, HUH?"

"THAT SETTLES IT! YOU'RE GOING TO BE AN ONLY CHILD!"

"HEY, DAD!"

"WHAT'RE YOU GOING TO BE, DENNIS, IF THE NEIGHBORS LET YOU GROW UP?"

THE 1950s

"YOU WOULDN'T LAUGH IF HE WAS WEARING YOUR SHOES AND STOCKINGS!"

"NEXT TIME I SNEAK YA SOME LIVER, EAT IT! DON'T DRAG IT AROUN' THE ROOM!"

"LOOK, DAD! RUFF FOLLOWED US TO CHURCH!!"

"WHY GET SO EXCITED OVER A LOUSY BONE?"

"PUT ALL THOSE BONES IN A BAG, WILL YA? I GOT A DOG WHO'S NEVER TASTED RESTAURANT FOOD!"

"TELL ME WHEN HE'S EATEN A NICKEL'S WORTH."

"WHAT'S MORE IMPORTANT....A NEAT KITCHEN OR FIRST PRIZE IN THE DOG SHOW?"

"AND THAT'S ALL MUSCLE, TOO!"

"I HOPE I LIVE LONG ENOUGH TO CAUSE HIM AS MUCH TROUBLE AS HE'S CAUSING ME!"

"WELL, THAT'S ONE LESS MOSQUITO!"

"... AND THAT'S HIS MOTHER RUNNING ALONG OVER THERE YELLING AT HIM."

"WE HAD A BET AND BILLY WON A HORSEBACK RIDE. YOU'RE THE HORSE."

"WANNA DRAW STRAWS TO SEE WHO PICKS UP MY TOYS?"

"HEY! MY MARTINI TASTES LIKE GINGER ALE!"

THE 1950s

"YOU'RE NOT FOOLING ME WITH THAT SILLY NOISE, DENNIS. I KNOW YOU DON'T HAVE A GOAT WITH YOU."

"IS THIS TOOTHPASTE OR SHAVING CREAM?"

"WELL, WE TOOK HIM FOR A CANOE RIDE. ANY MORE BRIGHT IDEAS?"

"I DON'T UNDERSTAND WHY YOU NEVER HEARD OF MY DAD. HE WAS A *SAILOR!*"

"WAIT 'TIL YOU SEE HOW NEAT WE'VE BEEN STACKING THE DIRTY DISHES, MOM!"

"I HAVE SOME FOLKS WHO WOULD LIKE TO LOOK AT YOUR HOUSE, MRS. WADE. IS THAT LITTLE TOW-HEADED NEIGHBOR BOY AROUND?"

"MOM, WOULD YOU EXPLAIN TO JOEY WHY BOYS DON'T PLAY WITH DOLLS? I FORGET."

"PLEASE, GEORGE! SHOW DENNIS HOW YOU USED TO PLAY 'SHINE ON HARVEST MOON'!"

"THAT WAS JUST FOR LAUGHS DAD. I'LL TURN IT ON SLOW THIS TIME."

THE 1950s

"HOW WOULD YOU AND YOUR WIFE LIKE TO DRIVE DOWN TO THE BEACH WITH ME?"

"THAT'S THEM!"

"IT'S EASY TO SWIM UNDERWATER. IT'S STAYIN' ON *TOP* THAT'S HARD!"

"C'MON! IT'S NOT *EARLY!* THE SEAGULLS ARE UP!"

"DON'T TAKE IT OFF! I TOL' JOEY YOU HAD A HAIRY CHEST!"

"YOUR GATE WAS LOCKED... SO I CAME THROUGH THE HOUSE."

"THEY WANT TOO MUCH FOR A ROOM. WHERE'S DENNIS?"

"DID I EVER SHOW YOU MY WALL SAFE, HENRY? I'M RATHER PROUD OF THE CAMOUFLAGE JOB!"

"WELL, GEE! THE BIRDS AREN'T USIN' IT!"

"WE RENTED A *BEACH* COTTAGE, AN' WE'RE NOT GONNA SHAVE FOR A *WHOLE WEEK!*"

P.S. This is *CHILDREN'S DENTAL HEALTH WEEK*

"IF NOTHING HAPPENS TO ME, NOTHING WILL HAPPEN TO YOU. OKAY?"

"YOU FILL YOUR SOCK WITH SAND, LIKE THIS, SEE? AND THEN ——— WHAM!"

"CAN'T YOUR CAR STAY OUTSIDE 'TIL THE JUNKMAN GETS HERE NEXT TUESDAY?"

"WE'RE JUST KILLIN' TIME 'TIL MY MOM BUYS A NEW PAIR OF SHOES."

"...AN' PUT A LOTA CHAIRS IN OUR LIVIN' ROOM, AN' MOM COULD PLAY THE PIANO, AN' YOU COULD SERMON, AN' I COULD COLLECT THE MONEY, AN' WE COULD KEEP IT! SEE?"

"COME ON BACK, YOU LITTLE CRY BABY! YOU'VE GOT TO LEARN TO TAKE IT!"

"OKAY.... NOW, GUN IT!"

"I AM NOT A BIG BRAVE MAN! I'M FIVE YEARS OLD AND I'LL SCREAM BLOODY MURDER IF YOU HURT ME!"

"GO AHEAD, DADDY—SQUIRT IT RIGHT IN HIS EYE!"

"BUT YOU LAUGHED WHEN MILTON BERLE DID IT!"

"DID YOU HEAR SOMEONE SAY 'HEY, STUPID!'?"

"I HOPE DENNIS DOESN'T WORRY THE SITTER TOO MUCH. HE HID FROM HER JUST AS WE WERE LEAVING."

"STAY AWAY FROM THAT KID WITH THE BLACK PANTS!"

THE 1950s

THE
1960s

"I SURE *LIKE* RESTAURANTS! WHEN YA SPILL A GLASS O' WATER THEY ACT LIKE IT WAS *THEIR* FAULT!"

ONE AFTERNOON AS I WAS
DRAWN OUT OF THE INKWELL,
I SAW SOMETHING THROUGH A
WINDOW THAT LOOKED LIKE A
JUMBO TEXACO SERVICE STATION,
WITH FOUR HUMONGOUS STARS
PERCHED ON TOP OF THAT NEARBY
BUILDING. "GLORIOSKI," AS MY
OLD PEN PAL LITTLE ORPHAN
ANNIE USED TO SAY, WE
WERE IN MOSCOW, AND
THIS WAS THE KREMLIN!
I DON'T REMEMBER GETTING THERE, BUT HANK SAID WE WERE
ON A MISSION... A HUMOR EXCHANGE, IF YOU CAN BELIEVE IT.
BUT THEN AND THERE, IT DAWNED ON ME THAT WHEREVER HANK
WENT, LIKE MARY'S LITTLE LAMB, I WAS SURE TO GO.

FOLLOWING IN HANK'S FOOTSTEPS TOOK ME INTO MANY STRANGE
COUNTRIES, AND THEN ONE DAY HE ANNOUNCED THAT WE WOULD UNPACK
FOR A PROLONGED STAY IN SWITZERLAND OF ALL PLACES. BUT I DIDN'T
GET MUCH OUT OF IT. I WAS NEVER ALLOWED TO PLAY WITH THE LOCAL
KIDS OR LEARN TO SPEAK THEIR FOREIGN LANGUAGE. AND HE STILL
DRESSED ME IN OSHKOSH! BUT, EVEN THOUGH THEY WERE HARD TO
FIND AND EXPENSIVE, I GOT ALL THE PEANUT BUTTER AND ROOT BEER
I SCREAMED FOR.

AND THE JOB WAS GETTING STEADIER AND STEADIER.

"WHICH ARE YOUR GUEST TOWELS, MRS. WILSON?"

"WE DON'T LIKE THE WAY YOU DRIVE!"

"LOOK, FOR THE LAST TIME: I DON'T BUY BUGS!"

"WHEN ARE YA GONNA BE FINISHED WITH THE SWIMMIN' POOL?"

"GEE, DON'T YA EVER GET *DIZZY* WORKIN' WAY UP HERE?"

"YA EVER NOTICE THAT LUNCH ALWAYS TASTES BETTER IN A *SACK?*"

"OKAY, I'LL WAIT OUT HERE, BUT DON'T BLAME ME IF YOU BUY ONE WITH A HORN THAT DON'T WORK!"

"THEY'LL EAT ANYTHING... TIN CANS, NEWSPAPERS, SPINICH, CARROTS, *ANYTHING!*"

"MUST BE A FOREIGN CAR."

"I'M RUNNIN' AWAY FROM HOME. IF YA WANNA SEE ME, I'LL BE IN MR. WILSON'S GARAGE."

"PRETTY SOON THERE WON'T BE ANY DIRT LEFT IN THE *WHOLE WORLD!*"

"AN' YA KNOW WHAT? ... WHEN MY DAD WAS LITTLE THEY DIDN'T EVEN HAVE *SPACE!*"

"I DON'T FEEL SO GOOD. I DRANK MOST OF A *WAVE!*"

"WOULD YOU STAND UP, DAD? THEY WANNA KNOW WHO CALLED 'EM *'BUMS'!*"

"WANNA HEAR A CRAZY *RULE* THEY GOT AT THIS BEACH?...."

"I FOUND IT RIGHT NEXT TO THAT LADY LYING ON HER STOMACH."

"...AND ONE FOR MY SWEETHEART!"

"I'LL *STARVE* FIRST!"

"GIRLS ARE ALWAYS AFTER *ME* TO PLAY HOUSE, TOO!"

"TELL HER I'M NOT HERE."

"GO ON, MARGARET...SAY 'BZZZZZ'."

"...AND *THIS* LITTLE PIGGY WENT 'WEE, WEE, WEE!' ALL THE WAY HOME!"

"NAW! SHE MEANS HE *CRIED* ALL THE WAY HOME!"

"HOW DO I SOUND, DENNIS? I'M TALKING ON A *PINK* TELEPHONE!"

"SOMEDAY I'M GOING TO BE IN SWAN LAKE!"

"YA BETTER LEARN TO *SWIM* FIRST!"

"NOW... LIFT YOUR CHIN... OPEN YOUR EYES A LITTLE MORE ... AND PULL IN YOUR TONGUE... "

"GEE, YOU MEAN RUFF'S LITTLE BLANKET MADE *ALL* THOSE CLOTHES RED?"

"NOW TRY NOT TO *LAUGH*!"

"OF *COURSE* IT'S NOT A REAL BATHROOM, DENNIS. IT'S JUST A DISPLAY OF . . . ."

DENNIS!"

"WILL YOU TELL *DAD* HE'S USING UP SPACE FIVE KIDS COULD WATCH TELEBISHION ON!"

"YOU MUST LEARN TO RELAX, MRS. MITCHELL. YOU SAY TO YOURSELF 'I AM CALM. I AM...'... *HEY, GET AWAY FROM THERE!*"

"SURE...SHE'S RIGHT HERE SHOWIN' US HER *BIRTHDAY SUIT!*"

"WHAT ARE THESE LITTLE THINGS THAT LOOK LIKE SPIDERS NEXT TO THOSE LITTLE THINGS THAT LOOK LIKE WORMS?"

*"LOOK AT THAT SMILE. I'LL BET HE'S DREAMING HE JUST TURNED THE HOSE ON SOMEBODY."

*"I DON'T KNOW *EXACTLY* HOW MUCH MONEY I'VE GOT. BUT IT'S ALMOST HALF A PIG!"

*"THAT'S THE KID I WAS TELLING YOU ABOUT. DON'T LET THE DISGUISE FOOL YOU!"

*"HE'S A THOROUGHBRED RUSSIAN WOLFHOUND."

*"DON'T LET HER KID YA. HE'S A *TALL POODLE!*"

THE 1960s

"WHAT'S THIS LITTLE STICK DO?"   "DID *I* DO THAT?"

"HEY, TOMMY! TURN ON CHANNEL 4! THERE'S TWO *NEW FUNNY GUYS* CALLED LAUREL AN' HARDY....!"

"WELL, YOU HAVE TO GIVE HIM CREDIT FOR ONE THING ... YOU COMPLETELY FORGOT ABOUT YOUR TOOTHACHE WHILE HE WAS HERE."

"...AND, SO, IN *SPITE* OF MR. WILSON, WHO SAID DENNIS WOULD NEVER LIVE TO SEE THIS BIRTHDAY....."

"QUICK! HAVE YOU SEEN A SMALL BOY ABOUT FIVE YEARS OLD WITH FRECKLES AND A LONG, WHITE BEARD?"

"BE REASONABLE, MARTHA! SANTA CLAUS *HIMSELF* WOULDN'T SPEND $12.98 ON DENNIS!"

"WHO WANTS TO GIVE MY MOM A SEAT 'FORE I STAND ON HIS SHOE?"

"MOM? ARE YA STILL IN HERE?"

"*SOME* ART PLACE! NOT EVEN *ONE* PICTURE OF SANTA CLAUS!"

"I WONDER WHAT THEY DO WHEN THE BASEMENT GETS FULL OF STEPS?"

"LITTLE BOY SAYS HE CAN'T WRITE, SO HE WANTS TO *TALK* WITH SANTA CLAUS!....."

"THANK YOU SO MUCH! I WOULDN'T HAVE UNDERSTOOD A *THING* WITHOUT YOUR SON'S EXPLANATIONS!"

"CLUE ME IN ON THE PLOT. BETWEEN TRIPS TO THE SNACK-BAR AND TRIPS TO THE BATHROOM, I'VE LOST THE THREAD."

"TAKE A CARD! ANY CARD! *NOT THAT ONE!*"

"LOOK, KID, I DON'T MIND YA DIPPIN' IN MY POPCORN, BUT WIPE YOUR HAND ON YOUR *OWN* PANTS, SEE?"

"IF NOBODY'S EVER BEEN TO THE MOON, HOW COME WE KNOW IT'S MADE OF GREEN CHEESE?"

"WOULDN'T THAT BE *BEAUTIFUL* OVER THE FIREPLACE?"

"...AN' MY DAD SAID HE COULD BEAT YOU AT GOLF ANY TIME HE WANTS TO!"

"I'LL HOLD YOUR SEAT, GRANDPA, IF YOU WANNA BUY SOME MORE POPCORN OR SOMETHIN'."

"WELL, *SOMEBODY* KEPT YELLIN' '*WAKE UP AN' LIVE A LITTLE*'....
SO HERE I *AM* !"

"SHE'S GONNA BE SORE AT ME! I WAS S'POSED TO WAKE HER
UP WHEN I HEARD YOU GUYS DRIVE IN !"

"HOW FIRM CAN I GET WITHOUT
ACTUALLY BELTING HIM ONE ?"

"I DIDN'T LIKE THE SITTER YA LEFT ME WITH!"

"...AND IT'S GOT A RED LIGHT AN' A GREEN LIGHT AN' .... AW, HECK, I GUESS IT'S GONE NOW...."

"LISTEN. DO YOU HEAR A HARMONICA?"

"RUFF'S NOT THE ONE THAT'S BARKIN'! HE'S JUST *ANSWERIN'*!"

THE 1960s

"COULD WE HAVE A MAN-TO-MAN TALK, HENRY?"

"I GUESS SHE'S WORSE THAN ME. I HEARD MY MOM TELL DAD THAT SHE'S BROKEN UP *TWO* HOMES!"

"OF COURSE WE PROB'LY WON'T STRIKE OIL THE *VERY FIRST TRY!*"

"DENNIS, WILL YOU *PLEASE* CLOSE THAT LUNCHBOX?!"

"GEE WHIZ, MOM! YA CAN'T HAVE A DOG SHOW WITHOUT *DOGS!*"

"HI'YA, MR. WILSON! BET YA DIDN'T KNOW IT'S *RAININ'* OUT!"

"HOW DO YA S'POSE THE TV PEOPLE FEEL WHEN THEY'RE SHOWIN' ALL THESE PROGRAMS AN' NOBODY'S WATCHIN'?"

"MOM, WOULD YOU EXPLAIN TO JOEY WHAT'S SO TERRIBLE 'BOUT DIRT? I FORGOT."

"I'LL BET IF I CAME IN HERE WITH A MUSTACHE AN' SMOKIN' A PIPE, YOU WOULDN'T ASK ME FOR THE MONEY *FIRST*!"

"I'M NOT GOING TO GIVE *ANYONE* THE RAZZBERRY! THIS IS A *DUCK CALL*!"

"'WON'T YOU COME HOME, BILL BAILEY'! NOT *BIG BELLY*!"

"JOEY, WILL YA QUIT WORRYIN' ABOUT WHO DONE IT? *ENJOY* IT!"

"HEY, LET ME **HELP** YA!"

"I **HAD** TO GIVE HIM SOMETHIN'! HE'S GOT THE SADDEST 'MEOW' YA EVER HEARD!"

"YA MEAN **THIS** IS WHERE YOU HAVE ALL THEM 'HARD DAYS' YOU BEEN TELLIN' US ABOUT?"

"WELL, FROM NOW ON YOU'RE GONNA HAVE TO PICK ON **YOURSELVES**!"

"GIVE THE BABY SITTER A PHONY TELEPHONE NUMBER. I'D LIKE TO FINISH *ONE* PARTY!"

"I UNDERSTAND LITTLE BOYS BECAUSE I HAVE TWO GRANDSONS."

"I GOT TWO *GRANDMAS* BUT I DON'T UNDERSTAND OLD LADIES!"

"MAMA AND DADDY ARE PAYING ME MONEY TO KEEP YOU SAFE FROM *HARM*, SWEETHEART, SO *DON'T MAKE ME CLOBBER YA!*"

"THAT'S MY SITTER. BOY, SHE SURE TAKES CARE OF SOME PRETTY BIG KIDS!"

"IT'S THE SITTER. SHE'S GOING TO SUE US!"

'SHE WAS A NICE OLD BABY SITTER. SHE HAD A LITTLE BOTTLE O' COUGH MEDICINE, AN' BOY, WAS SHE EVER *JOLLY!*'

"I HAD A CHOICE TONIGHT OF SITTING FOR DENNIS MITCHELL OR THE FOUR HORRIGAN CHILDREN, SO *NATURALLY* I...."

".... SO I SAID, 'MRS. MITCHELL, I'LL HAVE TO HAVE DOUBLE MONEY TO SIT WITH DENNIS!' AND SHE *PAID* IT!"

"YOU GOTTA ADMIT IT'S FASTER'N CARRYIN' WATER IN A LITTLE PITCHER!"

"DID YOU HEAR THAT, ALICE? HE MADE *TWO DOLLARS* BY SELLING..."

"SOLD MY *WHAT*?....."

"SURE, IT'S A NICE ROOM, BUT WHAT I'D *REALLY* LIKE IS A TENT!"

"BOY! JUST WHEN I THINK IT'S ALL JUNK, I FIND *THIS*!"

"HEY, MOM! I LEARNED HOW TO **WHISTLE!**"

"KNOW WHY THEY'RE SO BUSY HERE? 'CAUSE THEY DON'T SERVE **VEG'TABLES!**"

"BOY, ARE YOU PEOPLE LUCKY! MY DAD WASN'T SURE THE OLD CLUNKER WOULD MAKE IT DOWN HERE!"

"I DON'T MIND THE RAIN, NOR SNOW, NOR SLEET, NOR GLOOM OF NIGHT, BUT THAT KID ON MAPLE STREET IS **TOO MUCH!**"

"CAN'T YOU KEEP AN EYE ON HIM FOR A FEW DAYS?
HE'S GETTING AHEAD OF ME!"

"...AND WHEN YOU *DO* FIND HIM, WOULD YOU PLEASE RETURN THE APRON?"

"HEY! I BEEN *LOOKIN'* FOR THAT MARBLE!"

"BOY, A GUY WOULDN'T GET AWAY WITH *NOTHIN'*
IF HE HAD *FOUR* MOTHERS!"

"YA KNOW SOMETHIN'? I HAVEN'T HAD ANY FUN SINCE *YESTERDAY!*"

"WELL, I'M *NOT* YOUR LITTLE BOY! AN' I DON'T *WANNA* LEARN A THING OR TWO!"

"NAW, I DON'T WANNA TRADE. I'VE *SEEN* THAT ONE."

"THE ROLLING STONES DON'T GET HAIRCUTS! HERMAN'S HERMITS DON'T GET HAIRCUTS! THE REMAINS DON'T...."

"HOW LONG HAVE YOU BEEN WORKING FOR US, MOM?"

"YOU SURE GOT SOME NICE PEELIN' BANANAS HERE, MISTER!'

"GRANDMA WANTS TO TALK WITH HER 'LITTLE BOY'...."   "HIM?!"

"ARE WE *REALLY* FISHIN', OR JUST PRETENDIN'?"

"HEY, LADY! WHAT'S THE BIG IDEA KISSIN' MY *HORSE*?"

"WANT A SIP?"

"IT'S SWEET PICKLE JUICE."

"I HOPE THIS DON'T GO EXTRA INNINGS. I'M LIABLE TO GET *SICK*!"

"I'D TRADE EVERYTHING IN THERE FOR A PONY AN' TWO BALES O' HAY."

THE 1960s

"BOY! GRAMPA SURE KNOWS HOW TO TREAT LITTLE KIDS! HE SHOULDA HAD SOME OF HIS *OWN!*"

"I ONLY GOT A NICKEL. HOW 'BOUT MAKIN' ME A *SHORT* MILKSHAKE?

"...THAT'S TOMMY, THAT'S BILLY, AN' THAT'S JOEY. AN' WE'RE *ALL BROKE!*"

"HOW MUCH FOR A BANANA SPLIT IF I GOT MY *OWN* BANANA?"

"BOY, LET'S HOPE WE DON'T FIND ANOTHER FIVE DOLLAR BILL *TOMORROW!*"

"HI, MISTER WILSON! YOU SURE LOOK *LONESOME* UP THERE ALL BY YOURSELF!"

"I'LL HAVE IT OVER *HERE*, PLEASE!"

"BOY! HAVE YOU GOT A *TEMPER!*"

"HOW DO I KNOW HE'S BEEN MESSING WITH MY CAMERA? BECAUSE THERE ARE SIX PICTURES OF RUFF AND TWO OF JOEY. *THAT'S* HOW I KNOW!"

"I SURE HATE TO THINK A LITTLE OL' GOPHER CAN DIG FASTER'N *I* CAN!"

"LET ME *KNOW* WHEN WE GET TO *TEXAS.*"

"MOM WANTS TO SEE YOU IN THE KITCHEN! AN' SHE'S WEARIN' HER *MAD* FACE!"

"THAT'S THE BOY! STEADY DOES IT . . . . ."

"HE'LL BE HIS OLD SELF IN A COUPLE OF DAYS, SO *YOU'D* BETTER GET SOME REST, TOO!"

"GO BACK TO SLEEP. THE FLY IS *DEAD!*"

"I HAVTA SCRAPE SOME JELLY OFF MY BEDROOM CEILING."

"...AN' THEN YA LOOK UP AT THE SKY AN' YELL 'OH, NO!'"

"BUT WHY DO YA WANNA PLAY A GAME THAT MAKES YA MAD?"

"I DON'T THINK THAT THING IS DOIN' A BIT OF GOOD!"

"WE HAD A *SWELL* TIME! MR. FARISH AN' MR. McCLURE GOT MAD ABOUT SOMETHIN', AN' ME AN' DAD GOT TO PLAY ALL BY *OURSELF!*"

"YOUR SHAVIN' CREAM'S IN THE KITCHEN. THAT'S *CAKE FROSTIN!*"

"HE'S NOT QUITE FIVE, SO NATURALLY I DIDN'T THINK HE COULD MOVE THE LADDER WITH ME STANDING ON IT....."

"LOOK WHAT I FOUND! THEY'RE ALL OVER THE PLACE!"

"WHAT ARE YOU GONNA BUY WITH MY DAD'S QUARTER?"

"HI, MR. WILSON! GEE, I DIDN'T KNOW YOU EVER WENT TO CHURCH!"

"YOU KNOW WHAT HE SAID TODAY? HE ASKED ME IF HE COULD 'RING THE BELLS SOMETIME'!"

"WHILE WE'RE ALL IN A GOOD MOOD, MAYBE I OUGHT TO TELL YOU WHAT HAPPENED YESTERDAY."

"IS THIS BUYIN' US A TICKET TO HEAVEN?"

"HEY, MOM! IT'S THAT SUNDAY FELLA!"

"YOU SOUNDED A LITTLE HOARSE, SO I PUT A COUGH DROP IN THE COLLECTION FOR YA!"

"IT'S OKAY. HE DON'T BITE."

"WOW! FOUR DIFFERENT MOTHERS!"

"I GUESS THEY AREN'T GONNA GIVE US ANY DINNER. THERE'S NOTHIN' GOIN' ON IN THE KITCHEN!"

"HEY, THAT'S PRETTY FUNNY! LOOK, MADGE, HE'S WEARING FLOWERS IN HIS DAD'S ..... HEY! THAT'S MY HAT!"

"YOU 'FRAID OF MICE?"

"GEE, IF YA LIKE *THAT* KIND OF PITCHERS, I CAN GET YA A WHOLE KIDDIEGARTER *WALL* FULL!"

"I DIDN'T 'SPECT YOU TO USE A FORK. MOM SAID YOU ATE LIKE A 'BIRD'!"

"WHICH ONE IS NICK THE GREEK? MOM SAID TO TELL HIM HE'S GOTTA WORK TOMORROW."

"DUST IS DIRT THAT NOBODY CAN SEE EXCEPT YOUR MOM."

"THERE! *THAT* OL' FLY WON'T BOTHER YA AGAIN!"

"MOM, HOW MUCH SHOULD 1 CHARGE FOR CHICKEN LEGS?"

"DON'T THEY HAVE ONE CLOSER TO THE GROUND?"

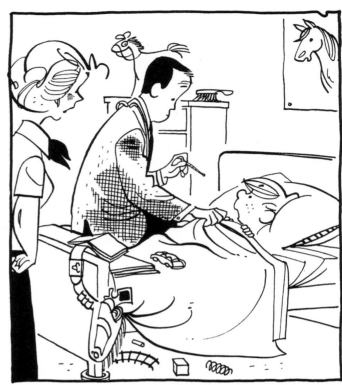

"* NOBODY EVER TOLD THE MARSHAL OF DODGE CITY WHEN HE HADDA EAT LUNCH!"

"....AN' THE JUNK SHE FEEDS ME! EGGS, CARROTS, MILK, GREEN SALADS!...DIDN'T YOU TELL HER I WAS *SICK*?"

"'I CAUGHT THE DOG. DID THE KID GET AWAY FROM YOU?"

THE 1960s

"'MOM SURE WAS GLAD TO GET THOSE FISH YOU GAVE US, MR. WILSON. SHE KNOWS A LADY THAT'S GOT *FOUR CATS!*"

"NOW ALL WE GOTTA DO IS FIND SOME DUMB KID THAT WANTS TO BUY FIVE POUNDS OF SUGAR, *CHEAP!*"

"THEY ALL HAVE PAPERS."

"YEAH. BUT WILL THEY *USE* 'EM?"

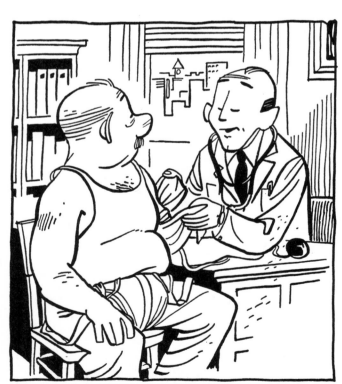

"THE LITTLE NEIGHBOR BOY MUST BE BEHAVING BETTER. YOUR BLOOD PRESSURE IS."

"DAD SAYS I CAN HELP HIM WASH THE CAR 'TIL I GET IN THE WAY!"

"LUCKY THING YOU'RE WEARIN' YOUR WASH 'N WEAR SUIT, HUH, DAD?"

"YA 'MEMBER THE SUN WENT DOWN OVER THERE? WELL, IT'S COMIN' UP OVER *HERE!*"

"I'VE BEEN CLEANING UP MY YARD, AND I THOUGHT YOU MIGHT SWAP ME THIS STUFF FOR MY HEDGE TRIMMERS?"

"*YOU* KICK THEM OUT. THEY JUST VOTED ME MRS. PRETTY OF 1960!"

"IT'S ONLY A FIRE ENGINE, CHILDREN, SO JUST LIE BACK DOWN AND — *DENNIS! COME BACK HERE! DENNIS!*"

"I REMEMBER THE DAY HE WAS BORN. I WAS FIFTEEN YEARS YOUNGER THEN."

"THEY'RE TALKIN' 'BOUT FOOTBALL. 40-23-36 IS *SIGNALS!*"

"I DON'T KNOW NOTHIN' ABOUT ART, BUT I KNOW A BANANA WHEN I SEE IT!"

and now...

Dennis the Menace in

FULL COLOR

Dennis the Menace
By Hank Ketcham
Farmer's Helper

"My mom says I gotta get rid o' my bugs!" "That's nice."

"HEY! What are you DOING?"

"She told me to take 'em back where I GOT 'em."

"WOW! Look at the SIZE of that watermelon!"

"And you thought I couldn't GROW anything!" "I guess I was wrong, Mr. Wilson."

"COME AND LOOK, MARTHA!! I DID IT!"

"I-I don't believe it!" "I TOLD you I was a first-class farmer!"

"NEXT year, I'm going to grow HUNDREDS of watermelons!"

"I'm going into the WATERMELON BUSINESS!" "Now calm down, George!"

"See this? I've got a GREEN THUMB!" "Careful, dear! It's heavy!"

"Isn't that the watermelon your father brought home last night?" "Huh?"

"BOY! Did you see how HAPPY he was, Mom?"

Dennis the Menace
By Hank Ketcham
'The Buckaroo Stops Here'

"Gee whiz, Mr. Wilson! How long are ya gonna read that dumb PAPER?" "That depends."

"On WHAT?"

"On how long you plan to STAY!!"

"I'll be the sheriff an' you be the bad guy, okay?" "Not on your life."

"All right, then, I'LL play the bad guy." "What do you mean PLAY?"

"Huh?" "You ARE the bad guy."

"But the sheriff is the best PART!" "I don't have a BADGE."

"NOW you've got one."

"An' if ya catch me, you can tar an' feather me an' run me OUTA TOWN!"

"WHOA! Ya gotta give me a HEAD START!"

"Good Heavens, George! Whatever possessed you to play cowboys with Dennis?"

"He just made me an offer I COULDN'T refuse."

Dennis the Menace By Hank Ketcham

Second-Story Man

It's such a **BEAUTIFUL** day! Why don't you boys play outside?!

I guess your mom wants us to get some fresh air, huh, Dennis?

I don't think it has anything to do with the weather, Joey.

Dennis the Menace By Hank Ketcham

Saving Face

You look very nice. Now, I want you to be courteous and well-behaved at the party.

You're not to race around or roughhouse or make messes or insult anybody. Do you understand?

Mom, have you got me mixed up with somebody else?

Dennis the Menace By Hank Ketcham

Idol Thoughts

When will I start to shave, Dad?

Not until you're in high school.

Ya mean if I don't go to high school I can't **SHAVE**?

Dennis the Menace By Hank Ketcham

Dennis Digs Mr. Wilson

Hey, Margaret! Take a look at this beauty!

Huh?

YIEEEEE

Girls sure are **SCREAMISH** about worms!

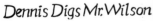

Dennis the Menace By Hank Ketcham

The Numbers Game

How 'bout playin' with me, Mr. Wilson?

I'm busy.

Yes, dear...he has to clean the garage, mow the lawn, and take out the garbage.

Good idea! Let's **PLAY**!

Dennis the Menace By Hank Ketcham
GOOD INTENTIONS

"I bet you can't name the four seasons."

"Sure I can!"

"Okay, what are they?"

"Salt, pepper, vinegar and mustard."

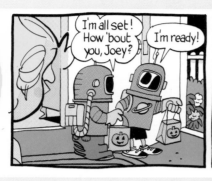

Dennis the Menace By Hank Ketcham
Spaced Out

"I'm all set! How 'bout you, Joey?"

"I'm ready!"

"Now, remember! Don't wander too far!"

"Don't worry, Mom..."

"...WE WON'T LEAVE THE PLANET!"

Dennis the Menace By Hank Ketcham
TUNED IN

"I think I hear the ice-cream truck!"

"I didn't hear a THING!"

"Ice-cream trucks are like DOG whistles..."

"...only KIDS can hear them!"

Dennis the Menace By Hank Ketcham
Second Offense

"Go to your room, young man!"

"And STAY there until dinner!"

"Okay! Okay!"

"HEY, MOM?"

"NOW what?"

"Can we have dinner EARLY?"

Dennis the Menace By Hank Ketcham
BAD CONNECTION

"Well, boys will be boys..."

"But that's not all... he sprayed shaving cream all over the bathroom!"

"He was an absolute TERROR today!"

"And no matter what my mom says, it was a GREAT day!"

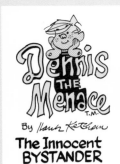

Dennis the Menace
By Hank Ketcham
The Innocent BYSTANDER

What's the rush, Dennis? / I got a feelin' Mrs. Wade's gonna call my mother!

But you don't wanna **BE** there, do ya? / Sure!

Why? / So I can answer...

...an' tell her she's got a **WRONG** number!

Dennis the Menace
By Hank Ketcham
MOMory Lane

There's no **ALICE** here.

Dennis! **I'M** Alice!

And here I've been calling her **MOM** all this time.

Dennis the Menace
by Hank Ketcham
'Copy Boy'

Dennis, what are you **DOING**?

Playin' with my **RADIO**.

Why didn't you **TELL** me you broke Mr. Wilson's window? / Why didn't ya tell **DAD** when you dented the fender on the car?

That's different. / How?

Never mind! What am I going to **DO** with you? / You could **HIDE** me!

You go right over and **APOLOGIZE**, young man! / Aw... okay!

I'm sorry I busted your window, Mr. Wilson.

Do you realize what windows **COST** these days? / A whole bunch?

This is the **THIRD** time you've broken a window!

Tell him how many windows you broke when **YOU** were a boy, George.

Well? How many **DID** you break, George?

5-29

Dennis the Menace
By Hank Ketcham

"... and puppy dog tails"

 "I just stopped by to wish you a nice day!" "How **SWEET!**"

 "Come in and have some milk and cookies!"

 "Thanks, Miz Wilson, but I'm cutting down on cookies an' stuff."

 "Who **WAS** that kid?!"

 "That's a very pretty dress you're wearin', Margaret!" "It **IS?**"

 "I mean... well... thanks, Dennis!"

 "**YOU** look great, too, Gina!"

 "See ya later, ladies. An' have a **SWELL** day!"

 "Are you sure that was **DENNIS?**"

 "Hi, Dennis! Wanna feel somethin' **GOOEY?!**" "Sorry, Joey."

 "I'm gettin' too **OLD** to play in mud puddles."

 "Wake up, dear! You've been talking in your sleep!" "Huh?"

 "**WOW!** You're not gonna believe the **DREAM** I just had!!"

Dennis the Menace
By Hank Ketcham

UNEASY RIDER

 "This vacation will do you a **LOT** of good, George..."

 "...to get out and see new **PLACES**..."

 "...and some new **FACES**...on people who don't eat you out of house and home."

 "Don't worry about your house, Mr. Wilson."

 "If any burglars break in, we'll call the cops."

 "And we won't let anybody pick your flowers."

 "And if there's a **FIRE**, we'll call the Fire Department right away."

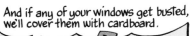 "And if any of your windows get busted, we'll cover them with cardboard."

 "And if any trucks crash into your house, we'll get the license number."

 "So don't worry about a thing." "George for heaven's sake... you're on vacation. **CHEER UP!**"

Dennis the Menace
By Hank Ketcham

Ballet-Hoo

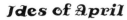

Dennis the Menace
By Hank Ketcham

Amtrash

These boxes are going out unless somebody has a use for them.

I can use 'em!

What are you going to *PUT* in them?

Me and my friends.

I'm an engineer! Wanna go for a ride on my train, Joey?

I can't. My Mom is callin' me.

HOP IN RUFF!

ALL ABOARD! Anybody?

Hi, Gina! Have a *FIRST-CLASS* train ride!

I'd love to, Dennis, but I have to go to the store.

Hey, Hotdog. How about it?...

...forget it.

Hey, Margaret! You're in *LUCK!* You can have a ride on a *TRAIN!*

I'm not sitting in any old box pretending I'm on a *TRAIN!*

WHO NEEDS THEM!

How do ya like my *FREIGHT* train, Mom?

8-21

Dennis the Menace
By Hank Ketcham

TRIPLE THREAT
TRIPLE THREAT
TRIPLE THREAT

That's a *PERFECT* fit!

Look in the mirror and see what you think.

I don't like *ANY* of 'em!

A woman in town just had *TRIPLETS!* ALL *BOYS!*

How would you like it if *I* were triplets?

8-25

HI, MOM!

HEY! Why's everybody so *QUIET?*

Dennis the Menace
By Hank Ketcham

Match Serve

 I gotta go home now, Miz Wilson.

 What's your hurry?

 It's SUPPER-TIME!

 I'm hungry. Where's Mom? / She's playing tennis with Margaret's mother.

 Playing? She should be makin' our DINNER!

 We could STARVE!

 Your mother gets tired of cooking and cleaning everyday. / Then why don't she take a NAP?

 I'm back, boys, I had a WONDERFUL game!

9-18

 Swell! but what's for SUPPER?

 This is my day off. NO COOKING!

 But my STOMICK'S empty.

 DING DONG

 I've got one pepperoni and one anchovy.

 Ya know what, Mom? You oughta get out and play more tennis.

Dennis the Menace
By Hank Ketcham

Borrowing TROUBLE

Run over and borrow a cup of sugar from Mrs. Wilson. / Okay, Mom.

Oops! CRAK!

Hi, Mrs. Wilson. Can I borrow a pocketful of sugar?

 Where did you get the neat cement truck, son?

 It's Joey's.

 He said I could BORROW it.

Don't get in the habit of BORROWING things, son...

...it can RUIN friendships. / Really? Gee!

 Dennis, ask your dad if I could borrow his pipe wrench.

 He says it might ruin your friendship if ya BORROW stuff.

 Is that SO? Then tell him to give me back my hedge clippers!

 Mr. Wilson said THAT? I'd better go out and smooth things over!

 Did Dad buy this book, Mom? / No, dear. He BORROWED it from the library. / Him an' me have gotta have a TALK!

Dennis the Menace By Hank Ketcham

Ruff and Ready

"He knows how to fetch sticks REAL GOOD, huh, Margaret."

"But you didn't THROW the stick!"

"Sure I did! I threw it yesterday and he just now decided to get it."

"Roll over, Ruff."

"But he was rolling over before you TOLD him to."

"Sure! Now watch him do THIS!"

"Okay, I'm watching."

"SCRATCH, Ruff!"

"Hey! Wait a minute! He was ALREADY scratching."

"STOP SCRATCHING, RUFF!"

"Oh, brother."

"That dog is DUMB and so are you!"

"NO WAY! Ruff is REALLY smart!"

"He knows what I'm gonna tell him to do before I even tell him to DO it."

Dennis the Menace By Hank Ketcham

Close Encounter

"I gotta HIDE, Mr. Wilson! Ol' Margaret's trying to give me a VALENTINE!"

"What's wrong with THAT?"

"Last year she tried to KISS ME!"

"Margaret's been CHASING me! How come she's gettin' so MUSHY!?"

"It's VALENTINE'S DAY, Dennis!"

"What's that got to do with it?"

"AMORÉ... Love..."

"Cupid is shooting his arrows!"

"Huh?"

"Valentine's Day brings out the ROMANCE in us!"

"Not ME!"

"Birds are singing, bees are buzzing and sap is running."

"But it's still WINTER!"

"An' the only SAP running around here is OL' MARGARET."

"OH NO! Here she comes!"

"What am I gonna do?"

"THANKS, Miz WILSON! I'll be back when the SAP stops running!"

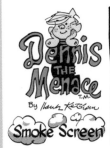

Dennis the Menace By Hank Ketcham — *Smoke Screen*

"Is Dad **REALLY** gonna stop smokin', Mom?"
"Yes, dear."
"Gosh! I thought that was hard to do!"
"Not for your father."
"He's quit smoking **DOZENS** of times."

Dennis the Menace By Hank Ketcham — *The Outdoorsman*

"This is a **GLASS** fishin' pole."
"Are you sure?"
"That's what my **DAD** told me."
"Do you believe him?"
"No."

Dennis the Menace By Hank Ketcham — *Father Time*

"Jim Hill's wife had another baby. It's their **FOURTH!**"
"**GOODNESS!** How would **YOU** like to have brothers and sisters, Dennis?"
"Well, at least, I wouldn't get **BLAMED** for everything!"

"What did people do when you guys were young?"
"I'm glad you asked, my boy! You won't believe this, but..."
"Here we go again!"
"...we used to sit on the porch and enjoy the peace and quiet of summer evenings!"
"Actually, it was noisy! Everybody had their radios turned up!"
"We listened to Fibber McGee, Fred Allen, Jack Benny..."
"...and swatted mosquitos."

"And sometimes I'd strum my ukelele..."
"Did he ever! He knew **THREE** chords!"
"And I'd sing, 'Meet Me Tonight in Dreamland,' and, 'Peg O' My Heart'..."
"He sounded like a lovesick **MOOSE.**"
"Why do you always try to **BUTT IN,** Martha?!"
"My mom rented a great movie for our VCR an' she says **YOU'RE** invited!"
"You got a **DATE** kid!"
"I'll pop a TV dinner in the microwave for the old fossil and be right over!"

8-6

"GEE, MRS. WILSON I DIDN'T KNOW *YOU* WENT TO BEAUTY SHOPS!"

"NO. I DIDN'T LEAVE THE SET ON. ARE YOU SURE *YOU* DIDN'T?"

"YOU KNOW HOW YOU KEEP SAYING WE SHOULD LIVE CLOSER TO OUR GRANDCHILDREN, TOM? WELL, *FORGET* IT!"

"GET OVER TO THE MITCHELLS, AND TAKE EDDIE WITH YOU. I GUESS THE KID'S REALLY GOT THE PLACE *FLOATIN'* THIS TIME!"

THE 1970s

"LET ME GET THIS STRAIGHT . . . YOU'RE THINKING OF SENDING THE **DOG** TO OBEDIENCE SCHOOL?"

OLD HANK APPARENTLY THOUGHT I WAS FEELING BORED AND A BIT BOXED-IN BY THE PANEL FORMAT. "LISTEN, KID," HE SAID, "I'VE GOT AN IDEA TO GIVE YOUR LIFE SOME CONTINUITY...WITH EVEN MORE PIZAZZ THAN THEY HAVE IN THE COMIC STRIPS." AND THEN HE SENT ME OFF ON A TWO-WEEK VISIT TO UNCLE CHARLIE'S FARM. HE NEXT ARRANGED FOR GRAMPA JOHNSON TO SPEND AN ACTION-PACKED WEEK WITH THE FAMILY, AND ONE AUTUMN, HE PRESSURED MY DAD INTO TAKING ME ON A CAMPING TRIP! NOW THIS WAS MORE *LIKE* IT!

IN 1976, FOR THE BICENTENNIAL, HANK SENT ME ON A TIME TRIP FOR A TWO-WEEK, SHOW-STOPPING JAMBOREE OF HISTORIC COSTUMES FOR EVERYBODY AND SOME AWESOME REVOLUTIONARY ADVENTURES, BUT THE MOST FUN THING EVER WAS WHEN HANK PUT ME ON MY VERY FIRST AIRPLANE RIDE. AND AFTER ALL THESE YEARS, I STILL TALK ABOUT IT. THOSE WERE THE GOOD OLD DAYS... FOR *BOTH* OF US!

HEY, YA WANNA KNOW SOMETHING? THE SEVENTIES WERE TOTALLY *RAD!*

"*HE* GOES WHERE *I* GO!"

"*DON'TCHA!?*"

"MAYBE IF WE TAKE HIM TO CHURCH WITH US, IT'LL MAKE HIM A BETTER CAT."

"HONEST, MOM, HE'S REAL SORRY... HE JUST DON'T KNOW HOW TO *LOOK* SORRY!"

"SO, YA FINALLY DECIDED TO COME HOME! WHAT HAVE YOU GOT TO SAY FOR YOURSELF?"

"MEOW."

"YOU NEED A HAIRCUT."

"HE NEEDS A SHAVE, TOO."

"PUT YOUR DOG ON. RUFF WANTS TO BARK AT HIM!"

"WE'LL HAVE A GLASS OF WATER AN' A BOWL OF WATER AN' A SAUCER OF MILK."

"Shhhh...one YOWL an' none of us gets ANYTHING!"

THE 1970s

"I GUESS THEY KEEP COMIN' UP TO SEE WHO'S TRYIN' TO CATCH THEM."

"WELL, MOM....LOOKS LIKE WE'RE GONNA HAVE DAD AROUND THE HOUSE FOR A WHILE."

"HOW COME YA ALWAYS CALL HIM 'ARNIE'? HIS NAME IS *HENRY*, ISN'T IT?"

"BOY, DAD! YOU SURE LOOK *GOOD* WHEN YOU DON'T HAVE NO BALL TO HIT!"

"I KNOW WHERE WE CAN CATCH A COUPLE OF SWELL HAMBURGERS."

"IT'S GONNA COME IN HANDY SOME TIME WHEN I NEED A ROCK JUST THIS SIZE."

"*TYING* FLIES? AT MY HOUSE WE *SWAT* 'EM!"

"THAT'S *TWO TREES IN A ROW* YOU HIT, DAD! YOU'RE GETTIN' BETTER 'N *BETTER!*"

"LET'S ALL BE HAPPY-GO-LUCKY TONIGHT AN' NOT GIVE A HOOT WHAT ANYBODY EATS. OKAY?"

"I DON'T HAVE NO MONEY, BUT HOW 'BOUT A DEAL? I'LL ASK MY MOM IF YOU CAN EAT LUNCH AT OUR HOUSE."

"Was that the part kids aren't s'posed to watch?"

"OH, *THERE* YA ARE, MR. WILSON! THE WAY YOUR PHONE JUST KEPT RINGIN', I THOUGHT FOR A MINUTE YOU MIGHT BE ASLEEP."

"THOSE DARK CLOUDS ARE THE FULL ONES COMIN' IN AND THE WHITE ONES ARE EMPTIES GOIN' OUT."

"I DON'T **DRINK** AN' I DON'T **GAB**...SO WHY CAN'T I START **EATIN'**?"

"I'M IN NO HURRY TO LEARN HOW TO READ. I DON'T WANT A LOT OF **SIGNS** BOSSIN' **ME** AROUND!"

"MR. WILSON IS COMING OVER, DAD. YOU MIGHT BE THINKIN' OF SOMETHING NICE TO SAY TO COOL HIM DOWN."

"THAT ROAD HOG YOU JUST PASSED TURNED ON A BIG, RED LIGHT."

"KNOW WHY I LIKE HAMBURGERS BEST? EVERYBODY JUST EATS 'EM WITHOUT NO ARGUMENTS."

"WANT ME TO TELL HIM OFF, DAD? HE WOULDN'T CLOBBER A LITTLE KID."

"WITH ALL THE ARGUMENTS WE HAVE IN THE CAR... YOU THINK WE OUGHTA SIT THAT CLOSE TOGETHER?"

" I'M HUNGRY AN' THIRSTY... AN' I'M TIRED OF PLAYIN' WITH MY TOYS... AN' I HAVE TO GO TO THE BATHROOM!"

" YECCH! IF DAVY CROCKETT HAD STOPPED HERE TO EAT, HE NEVER WOULDA *MADE* IT TO THE *ALAMO!*"

"REMEMBER....IF THEY EVER STOP TO ASK YA QUESTIONS, JUST SAY YOU'RE *CLEAN!*"

"AW, MOM ... WE CAN'T GET THE CHRISTMAS SPIRIT JUST LOOKIN' AT *LADIES'* STUFF !"

" VERY NICE, DENNIS."

"WHAT A HAUL !"

"YOU CAN MAIL MY LETTER TO SANTA IF YOU WANT ... BUT I'D FEEL BETTER IF YOU SENT IT STRAIGHT TO GRANDPA."

"YEP, JOEY ... WE'RE READY WHENEVER *HE* IS !"

"MAKE A WISH."

'HOW 'BOUT THAT... IT'S *SNOWIN'!*'

"I'M GIVIN' ALL MY OLD TOYS TO THE SALBATION ARMY SO SANTA CAN BRING ME A FRESH BATCH OF *EVERYTHING!*"

"IT'S LIKE DIFFERENT SUNDAY SCHOOLS, JOEY... THEY ALL WORK FOR THE SAME GUY, BUT EACH ONE'S GOT HIS OWN CORNER."

"DON'T *BITE* HIM, HUH? I SORTA PROMISED HIM YA WOULDN'T."

"DON'T SHOOT HIM! HE WAS AIMIN' AT *ME*!"

"SORRY, DAD...I TRIED NOT TO LAUGH BUT IT CAME OUT MY **NOSE**!"

"WHEN THEY WORK IN A GREAT PLACE LIKE THIS, HOW CAN THEY EVEN **THINK** ABOUT WHOSE TURN IT IS TO GO TO LUNCH?"

"WHAT *FOR*? YOU ALREADY KNOW WHAT I LOOK LIKE...AND NOBODY ELSE **CARES**!"

"HE'S ONE-OF-A-KIND, ALL RIGHT. AND SO'S HIS DOG."

"MY MOM GETS BOOKS FROM THE LIBERRY, BUT SHE TAKES 'EM **BACK**."

"THE WORLD JUST DON'T WORK THAT WAY, JOEY. NOBODY **EVER** GETS SENT TO BED WITHOUT TAKIN' A BATH!"

"IN MY COLORING BOOKS THEY'RE ALWAYS *SMILING!*"

THE 1970s

"*ORANGE PAINT* ALL OVER HIM!"

"IT'S ALL THEM *CARROTS* COMIN' OUT!"

"I GUESS HE KNOWS HIS OWN FATHER, BUT WE WERE EXPECTING A MUCH BIGGER MAN."

"I KEPT MAKIN' *HIM* NERVOUS AN' HE KEPT MAKIN' *ME* NERVOUS SO WE CALLED THE WHOLE THING OFF!"

"I'M TIRED OF BEING THIS LITTLE! CAN'T WE MOVE INTO A HOUSE THAT'S GOT HIGHER FLOORS?"

"AREN'T YA GONNA MAKE ME GO TO BED PRETTY SOON?"

"IT DON'T LOOK UNBREAKABLE TO *ME*!"

"YES, IT'S ALL RIGHT FOR YOUR NEW FRIEND WALTER TO WATCH TV WITH YOU."

"*THIS* IS WALTER?"

Dennis visits THE FARM

"WE BETTER WATCH OUR STEP THIS WEEK, SARAH. WE GOT A REAL CITY SLICKER STAYIN' WITH US!"

"THERE'S ONE THING YOU'LL ALWAYS FIND ON A FARM, DENNIS... PLENTY OF *FRESH VEGETABLES!*"

"YEAH, BUT I LIKE IT HERE ANYWAY!"

"IF I WAS HOME NOW, I'D STILL BE TRYIN' TO GET MY MOM AN' DAD OUT OF *BED!*"

"GEE, UNCLE CHARLIE, YOU GOT THE *BIGGEST* BACKYARD I *EVER* SAW!"

"HOW COME YA STAY AROUND THE FARM ALL DAY, UNCLE CHARLIE? DON'T YA EVER HAVE TO GO TO *WORK*?"

"OH, BOY! I'M GONNA TELL DAD TO TRADE OUR CAR IN FOR ONE O' *THESE!*"

"THEY HAVE TO GET THEIR MILK THIS WAY ON THE FARM 'CAUSE THE MILKMEN DON'T DRIVE *OUT* THIS FAR!"

"IF YOU WANT TO *RIDE* OLD NELLIE I GUESS IT'S ALL RIGHT. BUT SHE DON'T NEED NO *BUSTIN'!*"

"MY END'S DOIN' OKAY, JOEY. IT'S *YOUR* END THAT'S DRAGGIN'!"

"AN' IT GOT A STICK-SHIFT AN' BUCKET SEAT AN' A *ZILLION* HORSEPOWER JUST LIKE A REAL *SPORT CAR!*"

"ONE IS FOR PASTORIZED, ONE IS HOMOGERIZED, ONE IS SKIM AN' I GUESS THE OTHER ONE MUST BE FOR CREAM."

"GEE, UNCLE CHARLIE, YOU'RE THE ONLY GROWN-UP I KNOW THAT 'PRECIATES *GOOD DIRT!*"

"WE KEEP HIM PENNED UP BECAUSE HE'S GOT A REAL BAD TEMPER."

"I WONDER IF MRS. WILSON EVER THOUGHT ABOUT THAT?"

"I DIDN'T MISS A *THING!* MR. WILSON SAYS THE NEIGHBORHOOD WAS *REAL QUIET* WHILE I WAS AWAY!"

"GEE WHIZ! IF **YOU** DON'T KNOW WHOSE LITTLE BOY I AM, WHO *DOES*?"

"IF THEY **DO** HAVE WARS, THEY'RE AWFUL QUIET ABOUT IT, JOEY."

"HOW DO THEY EXPECT PEOPLE TO GO TO THE BATHROOM IF THEY DON'T HAVE NO *COMMERCIALS*?"

"HE'S NOT JUST THE BEST OF HIS BREED...HE'S THE **ONLY**!"

"HOW LONG HAS HE BEEN IN JAIL?"

"MOM! HOW DO YA GET KETCHUP OUT OF THIS BOTTLE?"

"NEVER MIND...I GOT IT. *DON'T COME IN HERE!*"

"Yeah, an' not only their voices...when my Dad's sore at me, his **FEET** sound louder, too!"

DO NOT
FEED THE
ANIMALS

"NO *WONDER* THEY ALL LOOK SO SKINNY!"

THE 1970s

"THERE'S TOO MUCH *KISSIN'* IN YOUR MOVIE AN' NOT ENOUGH *BUTTER* ON YOUR POPCORN!"

"Mom...how many good years have I got left before somebody *MARRIES* me?"

"WHERE ARE YOU PEOPLE GONNA *MOVE* TO WHEN I GET MARRIED AN' HAVE A FAMILY OF MY OWN?"

"BOY! WHEN I THINK OF ALL THE IMPORTANT STUFF I COULD BE DOING!"

"I GOT TROUBLES ENOUGH WITHOUT GETTIN' MARRIED AN' HAVIN' A WIFE AN' TWO FATHERS AN' TWO MOTHERS."

"IT'S PROLLY HIS SISTER AND HE'S JUST BEIN' NICE TO HER."

"IF I EVER HAVE A GIRL FRIEND, I'M NOT GONNA HOLD HER UP! SHE'S GONNA LEARN TO WALK BY HERSELF!"

"HE DIDN'T *REALLY* KISS HER... THEY GOT STUNT MEN FOR THAT KINDA STUFF."

"SURE, HE LOOKS HAPPY *NOW*....BUT WAIT 'TIL HE FINDS OUT
HE'S GOTTA GO TO *WORK* EVERY DAY!"

"WHEN DO I GET MY HARMONICA BACK?"

"DO YA WANT YOUR ROOT BEER
STRAIGHT UP OR ON-THE-ROCKS?"

"CAN I STILL GET INTO HEAVEN FOR HALF PRICE?"

"HAVE I BEEN PASTEURIZED?"

"THE MUSIC IS TOO SLOW AND THE COMMERCIALS ARE TOO LONG."

"THAT KID IS A NATURAL-BORN CRITIC."

"NO, SIR. I HAVEN'T BEEN FIGHTIN'. THIS IS JUST NORMAL, EVERDAY WEAR AN' TEAR!"

"It's the Star Spangled Banner! He's been watching the *Late, Late* Show again!"

"No use tryin' to kid *YOU*.... You know I done it."

"Now look what you've done! I had that trap all set for the *Tooth Fairy*!"

"The kinda luck I've been havin', I figured *YOU* must be sore about somethin', too!"

"IT WASN'T REALLY MY FAULT....BUT I GUESS YOU HEAR THAT ALL THE TIME."

"I'M HAVING A PRETTY GOOD SLEEP. HOW ABOUT *YOU*?"

"...AN' BLESS GOLDILOCKS AN' BLESS SIMPLE SIMON AN' BLESS LITTLE MISS MUFFET AN' BLESS DEEDLE DEEDLE DUMPLING MY SON JOHN AN' BLESS...."

"THAT BLACK THING IN THE MIDDLE OF YOUR EYE GOT REAL TINY ALL OF A SUDDEN."

"SORRY, WE'RE OUT OF ROOT BEER."

"THEN I'LL HAVE A GLASS OF KETCHUP."

"I'M GONNA BE A *ANGEL* IN THE SUNDAY SCHOOL PLAY! HOW DOES *THAT* GRAB YA?"

"GOSH, DAD...TELL MOM WHAT THE WORLD IS COMIN' TO, SO SHE CAN START DINNER!"

"I'M THROUGH. WHILE YOU'RE FINISHING, I'M GONNA TAKE UP A BONE COLLECTION FOR RUFF."

"DAYS ARE REAL *NICE* BEFORE THEY BEEN USED!"

"HERE'S YOUR TROUBLE, LADY. PEANUT BUTTER ON YOUR VERTICAL RECTIFIER."

"I THINK I'LL GO BACK TO TAKIN' *NAPS* IN THE AFTERNOON."

THE 1970s

"I DON'T WANTA BUY NOTHIN'... I JUST WANTA *FEEL* SOME OF THE STUFF I CAN'T TOUCH AT HOME."

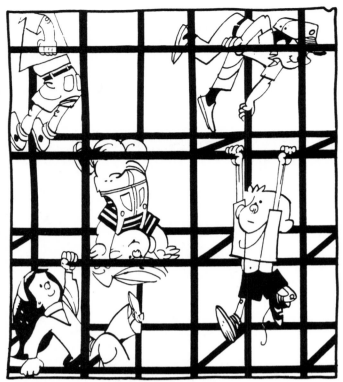

"MAYBE I'LL **NEVER** GO TO SCHOOL ... MY FOLKS KEEP TELLIN' ME NOT TO BE SO SMART."

"I CAN'T SETTLE DOWN TO WORK YET. GUESS I'M STILL TOO FULL OF SUMMER."

"HE CAN'T BE *THAT* BAD, MISS PRINGLE ... WE'VE NEVER EXPELLED *ANYONE* FROM KINDERGARTEN."

"HE'S *RUINED* NOW, BUT YOU SHOULDA SEEN HIM WHEN HE WAS A *STAR!*"

"I'M NOT SLEEPY, EITHER ... WHY DON'T YOU AN' ME PLAY CARDS OR SOMETHIN'?"

"LOOK, MOM ... I CAN JUGGLE **THREE EGGS** AT ONCE!"

"YOU SHOULDN'T HAVE **YELLED** LIKE THAT!"

"FALL IS KINDA LIKE A BUMPER, JOEY ... IT KEEPS SUMMER FROM BANGIN' RIGHT SMACK INTO WINTER."

"HOW'D YOU LIKE TO BE THE JOLLY GREEN MIDGET?"

THE 1970s

"GEE WHIZ... I THOUGHT YOU WAS FIGHTIN' WITH *BURGLARS*, OR SOMETHIN'!"

"I *THOUGHT* I HEARD A BIG FIGHT DOWN HERE LAST NIGHT!"

"HOW CAN YOU SIT THERE AN' *MUSH*, WHEN WE COULD BE TOASTIN' MARSHMALLOWS OR ROASTIN' WEENIES?"

"BOY, DAD SURE KISSES FAST! IF YOU HADN'T BEEN STANDIN' RIGHT HERE, YOU WOULDA *MISSED* IT!"

"YES, HENRY... WHY **DON'T** YOU GET ONE WITH A MOUNTAIN LION OR A GRIZZLY BEAR ON IT?"

"HOW'S THE CLIMATE?"

"STILL CHILLY, BUT WARMIN' UP A LITTLE."

"JUST SPILL A LITTLE ROOT BEER ON THE SOFA AN' YOU'LL FIND OUT HOW **SWEET** SHE IS."

"I HAD A GOOD FIGHT GOIN' FOR AWHILE...BUT THEY DECIDED TO KISS AND MAKE UP, AND NOW IT'S *LONESOME* AROUND HERE."

"ALL RIGHT...WHO'S SINGING POP GOES THE WEASEL WHILE THE REST OF US ARE SINGING GOD SAVE THE KING?"

"GO BACK TO SLEEP, ALICE... IT'S JUST SOME DRUNK ON A HORSE YELLING SOMETHING ABOUT THE BRITISH ARE COMING."

Dennis Celebrates The BICENTENNIAL

"A TORY IS SOMEONE WHO STILL THINKS KING GEORGE IS A GREAT GUY, JOEY."

"THEY SURE DON'T MAKE STUFF LIKE THEY USETA, HUH, MOM?"

"YOU MEAN THIS GUY IS GONNA LIVE HERE WHETHER WE LIKE IT OR NOT?"

"YOU'RE NOT GONNA LIKE IT."

"...AND BLESS GEN'RAL WASHINGTON AND HIS HORSE AND ALL OUR SOLDIERS AND EVEN OL' KING GEORGE ...BUT NOT AS MUCH."

"YOU CAN'T MISS HIM. HE WEARS SQUARE GLASSES."

"HE'S PROBABLY OUT FLYIN' HIS KITE!"

"WE HAD A PURTY GOOD MORNIN'...ME AND JOEY LICKED A COUPLE OF TORY KIDS, AND OL' RUFF BIT A TAX COLLECTOR."

"THEY DON'T SCARE ME NONE...HOW FAST CAN THEY RUN WEARIN' ALL THAT STUFF?"

"DAD SAYS IT'LL SEEM FUNNY NOT HAVIN' A **KING** TO KICK AROUND NO MORE."

"IT'S SO PEACEFUL UP HERE, ALICE... I WONDER IF MR. BUNKER WOULD SELL US A BUILDING LOT ON HIS HILL?"

"POLISH YOUR BUCKLES, KEEP YOUR BREECHES CLEAN... TAKE A BATH EVERY WEEK WHETHER YA NEED IT OR NOT..."

"CHEER UP, MR. WILSON! PRETTY SOON YOU'LL BE CUTTIN' GRASS AND PULLIN' WEEDS AGAIN."

"HOW 'BOUT IF I GIVE 'EM 'TIL SIX O'CLOCK TO CLEAR OUTA THE HOUSE?"

"ALL I WANT IS A GLASS OF WATER. AND COULD YOU PUT A LITTLE CHOCOLATE SYRUP IN IT?"

"I DIDN'T SAY HE *DID* IT...I SAID HE *COULD* HAVE DONE IT."

"I NEVER PUT ONE OF THOSE THINGS IN MY MOUTH UNLESS IT'S GOT A *ICE CREAM BAR* ON IT!"

"WHEW! AS THEY SAY, MRS. MITCHELL... ALL SYSTEMS ARE **GO** FOR ANOTHER SIX MONTHS."

"WHY CAN'T WE GIVE THE TOOTH FAIRY A QUARTER TO LET ME KEEP IT IN?"

"YOU CAN PULL YOUR TONGUE BACK IN NOW. THIS IS AN EXAMINATION .... NOT AN OPINION POLL."

"WHEN YA YELL 'HOT CHOCOLATE AN' COOKIES', IT CARRIES A *LONG WAYS* IN THIS WEATHER."

"MR. WILSON SAYS THIS USED TO BE A NICE, QUIET NEIGHBORHOOD, BUT THAT WAS BEFORE MY TIME."

"THIS IS THE FIRST CHAIR I EVER OWNED. THEY SURE BUILT 'EM *FUNNY* IN THOSE DAYS!"

"A VACATION? *NOW*? AN' MISS SOME OF THE BEST WEATHER WE'VE HAD ALL YEAR?"

"I'M AFRAID THE NEW MATTRESS HAS ALREADY BEEN DELIVERED. I CAN HEAR VOICES IN THE BACKGROUND GOING '*WHEE!*'"

"WOW! AN' THEY GET *PAID* FOR DOIN' THAT!"

"TELL THE GREAT LOVER HIS CAT FOOD IS READY."

"BOY! WAIT 'TIL YOU SEE THE SURPRISE MOM'S GOT FOR *YOU!*"

"HOWDY...HAVE YOU GOT A PICTURE OF THAT TOTEM POLE YOU'RE LOW MAN ON?"

"I KNOW THIS NEIGHBORHOOD PRETTY GOOD... JUST *WHICH* HILL ARE YOU OVER?"

"MY DAD WAS *RIGHT!* HE SAID YOU'D SHOW UP COME **BAD WORD** OR HIGH WATER!"

"IF HE'S NOT *MY UNCLE*, WHY DID YA SAY 'OH, BROTHER!' WHEN HE RANG THE BELL?"

"WHAT KIND OF STUFFIN' DO YOU *HAVE* IN YOUR SHIRT?"

"How can ya tell when he's hemmin' from when he's hawin'?"

"WHEN YOU TAKE 'EM TO THE CLEANERS, DAD, WILL YOU PICK UP SOME *ICE CREAM*?"

"I UNNERSTAND THIS IS YOUR FIRST SQUARE MEAL SINCE YOU GOT MARRIED."

"MR. WILSON SAID HE HOPES I GET SOME COAL IN MY CHRISTMAS STOCKING.... WHAT'S **COAL**?"

Peace & happiness

❋

forever and ever

❋

Hank Ketcham

"THIS IS WHAT THEY CALL THE **BOTTOM LINE**, JOEY...

"YOU'RE TOO LATE WITH THE CAMERA! HE'S **GONE**!"

"No use me worryin'...if anybody can handle a heavy sleigh in a snow storm, it's gotta be **HIM**!"

"Christmas Eve is the kinda dark I'm not scared of."

"The tree is holdin' up pretty good, but my Mom and Dad are beginnin' to droop a little."

"How much cheer can I spread for forty-seven cents?"

"HE SAYS HE FEELS SO WELCOME!
WHAT AM I DOING *WRONG*?"

"MY LITTLE TRUCK IS OKAY, MR. WILSON...
ARE *YOU* ALL RIGHT?"

"HEY, MR. WILSON! YA WANNA BREAK THIS WISHBONE WITH ME?"

snap

"WHAT DID YA WISH?"

"NO USE CALLIN' MY FOLKS, MR. WILSON. THEY DON'T
KNOW WHAT GETS INTO ME *EITHER*!"

"GEE... NO, MR. WILSON. I CAN'T MAKE *MYSELF* DISAPPEAR! I'M NOT *THAT* GOOD YET!"

"HI, MR. WILSON... HOW'S MY COLD?"

"BOOP-BOOP-A-DOOP MEANS THE SAME THING AS YEH-YEH-YEH."

"I'M NOT WORRIED ABOUT *BURGLARS*... I WANT A LOCK A *KID* CAN'T OPEN."

"YOU MEAN YOU PAID *EXTRA* TO GET
A DOLL THAT DOES *THAT*?"

"I'M GOING TO APPEAR
ON *TELEVISION!*"

"*GOOD!* THEN I CAN
TURN YA *OFF!*"

"IMAGINE *HER* KNOWIN' A WORD LIKE *THAT!*"

"IT'S JUST A FRIENDLY LITTLE SHOWER, MARGARET!
WHY DON'T YA LEARN TO *LIVE* A LITTLE?"

"ALL THE-ALL THE OUTS IN FREEEE !"

"I WONDER HOW LONG SHE'S GONNA KEEP THAT UP."

"SHE'S SEVEN YEARS OLD AND STILL HAS ALL HER TEETH !"

"HO HO! THAT'LL BE THE DAY, MARGARET! THAT'LL BE THE DAY !"

"I DON'T THINK IT'S CUTE. I THINK IT'S *PITIFUL !*"

THE 1970s

"WHAT'S SO GREAT ABOUT SEEING MARGARET IN ONLY 60 SECONDS? I'D RATHER WAIT."

"OOOH...WHAT A BOOFUL LI'L KITTUMS."

"PERSONALLY, I WOULDA *SCRATCHED* YOU."

"IF I EVER GET ENGAGED...WHICH I WON'T...I'LL BUY THE GIRL SOMETHIN' WE CAN **BOTH** ENJOY."

"If that's the one who isn't housebroke, keep her away from ME !"

"I TOLD YA A HUNNERD TIMES... HE'S NOT A DOLL! HE'S A STUFFED FRIEND."

"THAT'S GIRLS FOR YA. SHE'S GOIN' HOME TO TAKE A BATH, AND NOBODY EVEN CALLED HER!"

"HOW SWEET IT IS, JOEY... I GOT A DOG, A CAT, A MOM AN'A DAD AND MARGARET ISN'T TALKIN' TO ME!"

"WOULDN'T YOU SAY THE FILM WAS BETTER THAN THE TV VERSION, BUT DIDN'T MEASURE UP TO THE ORIGINAL COMIC BOOK STORY?"

THE 1980s

"DO YOU WANT TO HEAR ABOUT THIS NOW, OR
WAIT FOR THE TEN O'CLOCK NEWS?"

WELL, I DON'T RECALL THIS TRIP EITHER... I GUESS HANK TOOK A LONG BREATHER... BUT THERE I WAS BACK IN CALIFORNIA. WHEN FINALLY I WAS SUMMONED FROM THE INKWELL AGAIN, I SAW FOG DRIFTING ACROSS THE CYPRESS TREES AND HEARD THE BARKING OF SEA LIONS MINGLED WITH THE FAMILIAR GROANS OF GOLFERS IN AGONY... A FAR CRY FROM THE ALPS AND SWISS COWBELLS.

I WAS HAPPY TO BE BACK ON THE MONTEREY PENINSULA WHERE I FIRST SAW THE LIGHT OF DAY, AND HANK WAS ALL SMILES, TOO. HE NO LONGER NEEDED HIS WELL-THUMBED COLLECTION OF SEARS CATALOGS TO RESEARCH AMERICAN REFRIGERATORS, TOYS, AND TOILETS...

AND HE WAS ONLY A SMACK, CHIP, AND A PUTT FROM HIS FAVORITE GOLF COURSES.

THE EIGHTIES, HOW SWEET THEY WERE!

"DENNIS, THIS IS MRS. LURIE, THE DESIGNATED SITTER."

"WHY GET A SITTER? JUST CALL MR. WILSON! HE SAYS HE'S REALLY GONNA TAKE CARE OF ME ONE OF THESE DAYS."

"WASHINGTON AND LINCOLN WERE LUCKY TO HAVE THEIR BIRTHDAYS ON HOLIDAYS!"

"SHE'S GOT SOMETHIN' UP HER SLEEVE!"

"I KNOCKED THREE TIMES. I GUESS THERE'S NOBODY **IN** THERE!"

"IF YOUR WIFE'D SEW A NAME TAG IN YOUR SHIRT, MAYBE YOU WOULDN'T ALWAYS BE LOSING IT."

"IT'S EASY, JOEY. JUST GET A BIG ROCK AN' CHIP OFF ALL THE PIECES THAT DON'T LOOK LIKE A HORSE."

"I FORGOT. WAS PICASSO IN THE SECOND OR THIRD GRADE?"

"WHAT HAVE THOSE FROGS BEEN EATING TO MAKE SOUNDS LIKE THAT?"

"MY BIKE IS GONNA FEEL REAL *SKINNY* AFTER THIS!"

"I TOOK OUT THE CAR-LIFTER SO YOU COULD GET MORE SUITCASES IN THE TRUNK."

"LOOK, MOM! ALL THE TREES ARE GOING BACK HOME!"

"THAT'S THE FIRST TIME I EVER ATE SOMETHIN' THAT TRIED TO EAT **ME** FIRST!"

"NOW LET'S RIDE THE LITTLE AIRPLANES, DAD!"

"WORMS DON'T HAVE A VERY GOOD JOB, DO THEY?"

"*FORTY-THREE DOLLARS* IN LONG DISTANCE CALLS?!"

"YES, SIR...TO A MR. WILSON."

" IT WON'T DO NO GOOD TO PROMISE ME STUFF. YOU GOTTA TALK TO MY MOM 'N DAD."

"I COULDN'T FIND THE LADDER."

"IS THIS ALL?"

"COULD YOU WRITE A LETTER TO SANTA AN' TELL HIM WHAT A GOOD BOY I'VE BEEN? YOU DON'T HAVE TO SIGN IT."

"THERE'S NO TRICK TO GETTIN' YOUR CHRISTMAS SHOPPIN' DONE EARLY WHEN YOU ONLY GOT A **DOLLAR** TO SPEND."

"I GOT A SWELL PRESENT PICKED OUT FOR MY MOM... NOW ALL I NEED IS FOUR HUNDRED AN' FIFTY DOLLARS."

"I DREAMED THERE WAS THIS GIGANTIC TURKEY, AN' ALL HE WANTED TO EAT WAS **US**!"

"YOU LEFT YOUR KITCHEN WINDOW UNLOCKED AGAIN, MR. WILSON!"

"WADE IN TILL IT'S UP TO MY KNEES, DAD."

"EH..I CAN'T PLAY NOW, TOMMY. I HAVE TO MARCH RIGHT UP TO MY ROOM."

"BOY! THIS PLACE LOOKS LIKE A DEAD PET SHOP!"

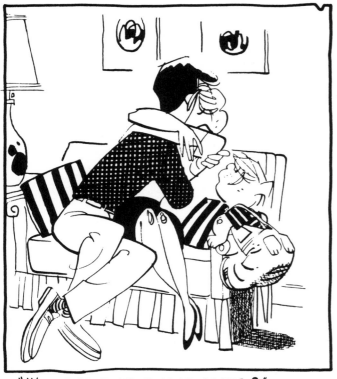

"WHERE DO YOU PUT YOUR NOSES?"

"LOOKS LIKE ALL YOUR TROUBLES ARE BEHIND YOU NOW, GEORGE."

"WHEN I STUCK THE WHATCHAMACALLIT INTO THE THINGAMAJIG, THE DOO-DAD POPPED AN' THE LIGHTS WENT OUT."

"...AN' WORSE THAN ANYTHING, MY YO-YO IS STILL UP ON THE ROOF!"

"YOU READY FOR DINNER? MOM JUST SOUNDED THE TWO-MINUTE WARNING."

"SHE'S MAKIN' A CAKE FROM A KIT."

"WHEN MR. WILSON'S HEAD SHINES, I KNOW THE CHILI IS GOOD AN' HOT."

"THEY'RE CALLED THE THREE B'S... BACH, BEETHOVEN AND BRAHMS."

"THEY FORGOT BROWNIES!"

"SHE'S COOKIN' LIVER AND CABBAGE. YOU WANTA COME WITH ME?"

"THAT NEW BABY ACROSS THE STREET DOESN'T TAKE A BOTTLE. HE EATS UNDER THE BRA."

"IF YOU WANNA STAY OUT OF TROUBLE, JUST EAT ALL OF YOUR CARROTS AND DON'T SAY NOTHIN'!"

"I KNOW I SHOULDN'T HIT GIRLS, BUT SHE SAID YOU WERE A LOUSY COOK!"

"MRS. WADE? YOUR DAUGHTER HAD IT COMING!"

"HER COOKIES ARE THE BEST 'CAUSE SHE PUTS IN SOMETHIN' CALLED 'INGREDIENTS.'"

"DAD JUST SWATTED A BLUEBERRY!"

"GOSH, GINA... YOUR MOM'S SOUP IS LIKE WHAT WE CALL DINNER AT OUR HOUSE!"

"I'D LIKE HALF THAT PIZZA WITH CHEESE AND THE OTHER HALF WITH DOG FOOD."

"GEE, MOM... HOW CAN YOU ALWAYS TELL WHEN I'M HUNGRY?"

"I'LL HAVE THE #2 BREAKFAST WITH TOAST AND ORANGE JUICE, PLEASE."

"WANT ANOTHER OYSTER, DENNIS?"

"I DODE EBEN WAD **DIS** ONE!"

"WON'T YOU BE SCARED 'WAY UP THERE?"

"NAW... I FEEL SORRY FOR ANY OLD WITCH THAT GETS IN FRONT OF A 747."

"I'VE FLOWN THREE TIMES ALREADY."

"BROOMS DON'T COUNT, MARGARET."

Dennis Takes His First Airline Flight

"DON'T **NEVER** THROW ROCKS AT AIRPLANES, JOEY! WHEN I GO TO VISIT MY GRAMPA, I'M GONNA BE SITTIN' BY A **WINDOW**!"

"WE'RE GOING TO **MISS** YOU, DENNIS."

"EVERY SINGLE, BLESSED DAY."

"I'M GONNA VISIT MY GRAMPA ...AN' WHEN WE COME BACK, WE MIGHT HAVE A **PONY** WITH US!"

"WHY CAN'T I BRING MY DOG?"

"NO TREES."

"WHEN WE'RE FLYIN' OVER CITIES, CAN WE USE THE BATHROOM?"

"WOW! I THINK I CAN SEE CLEAR INTO TOMORROW!"

"WHICH AM I... VACANT OR OCCUPIED?"

"I BEEN WANTIN' A HORSE FOR A LONG, LONG TIME... MAYBE YOU CAN HEAR ME A LITTLE BETTER UP HERE."

"WHICH WAY TO THE **POOL**?"

"YOU'D MAKE A **SWELL** MOM! YOU NEVER GET MAD, OR YELL, OR ..."

"JUST ONE MORE HOUR."

"WAKE ME UP IF WE SHOULD LAND ON THE MOON ... I WOULDN'T WANTA MISS IT."

"THEY'RE LOTS BIGGER *INSIDE* THAN THEY ARE *OUTSIDE*, JOEY... I GOT LOST THREE TIMES."

"THOSE PEOPLE WE HEAR LAUGHIN' SO MUCH . . .
ARE THEY WATCHIN' THIS SAME PROGRAM ?"

"HE BRINGS IT IN, I TAKE IT OUT! HE BRINGS IT IN,
I TAKE IT OUT..."

"WATCH, MOM! ANOTHER HOME RUN !"

"LOOK, DAD! THAT RIVER'S GOT
TOO BIG FOR ITS BRIDGES !"

"THAT WAS MY NEW BUGLE, MR. WILSON. HOW'D IT SOUND?"

"I GUESS THAT WAS A HAPPY ENDING. I KNOW I WAS GLAD WHEN IT WAS OVER."

"I REALLY GO TO KINDERGARTEN, BUT I TELL EVERYONE I'M IN BASIC TRAINING."

"BOY, I WISH WE COULD FAST FORWARD THIS DAY."

"I'LL SAVE YA A LOTTA TROUBLE: THE METS BEAT THE PADRES, THE RED SOX BEAT THE YANKEES, THE GIANTS..."

"YOU DON'T HAVE TO KISS HER TODAY. IT'S *SATURDAY!*"

"HE JUST FOUND OUT THAT SHIRLEY TEMPLE IS OLD ENOUGH TO BE HIS GRANDMOTHER."

"HE LOOKS LIKE THE SAME KID...DIDN'T YOU SAY YOU WERE GONNA *CHANGE* HIM?"

"WHEN A LADY NEVER MARRIES, SHE'S AN *OLD MAID.*"

"THEN WHEN A MAN NEVER MARRIES, IS HE AN OLD BUTLER?"

"DO YOU KNOW THE PORKY PIG THEME FROM LOONY TOONS?"

"I THINK MR. WILSON NEEDS A HUG."

"WOULD YOU ASK A LOT OF SILLY QUESTIONS IF I TOLD YOU I NEEDED FIFTY-SEVEN DOLLARS?"

"SEEMS LIKE OLD TIMES... YOU OUT THERE AND ME IN HERE."

"GEE, MR. WILSON, DON'T YOU REMEMBER ANYTHING BUT THE GOOD OLD DAYS?"

"MR. WILSON WON'T LISTEN TO ANYTHING HE HASN'T HEARD BEFORE."

"IS THAT A PICTURE OF MR. WILSON BEFORE HE WAS ENLARGED?"

"THAT'S THE KIND OF ENGINES THEY HAD BEFORE THE RAILROADS QUIT SMOKIN'."

"MMPH! THESE RECORDS ARE OLD AN' DRIED OUT. I CAN HARDLY *BEND* 'EM!"

"WAS THAT THE DAY *MOM* CAME TO WORK FOR US?"

"YOU BETTER HURRY HOME, MARGARET! IT WOULD BE *TERRIBLE* IF YOU GOT STUCK HERE IN A BLIZZARD!"

"JUST SLUSH, JOEY. THAT'S SNOW WITH ALL THE *FUN* TAKEN OUT."

"SUPPOSE YOU GET ALL THIS STUFF OFF AND I'M NOT **IN** HERE?"

"IT'S SNOWING OUTSIDE MY WINDOW, MR. WILSON! IS IT SNOWING OUTSIDE YOURS?"

"WE'RE READY, LORD... LET 'ER RIP!"

"I THINK THIS WINTER'S GETTIN' TOO *PUSHY*!"

WHAT'S A TOURIST, DAD? HAVE YOU EVER SEEN ONE?

NOT IN *THIS* PART OF THE COUNTRY.

"I'M JUST GIVING 'EM LEFTOVERS, SO ME AN' DAD AN' THE BIRDS WILL BE HAPPY!"

"THAT **LUMP** IS MY 'LECTRIC BLANKET."

"WHY'D HE TURN THE FROG INTO A PRINCESS? HE COULDA HAD MORE FUN WITH THE FROG!"

"NAW, I NEVER BOTHER TO CLEAN UP AROUND HERE. I HAVE A MOTHER WHO COMES IN A COUPLA TIMES A WEEK."

"ONE OF US IS GONNA HAVE TO LEARN HOW TO READ."

"...AN' BE SURE TO TELL JOHN WAYNE I SAID 'HI'."

"WHY SHOULD I HELP? YOU'RE THE ONE WHO WANTS IT CLEAN."

"DO YOU THINK GINA WOULD GET MAD IF I TOLD HER
I THOUGHT SHE WAS PRETTY?"

"WE DON'T KEEP RUFF'S BONES IN THE CUPBOARD!
THAT HUBBARD LADY MUSTA BEEN A NERD!"

"HEY, WAIT A MINUTE! WE'RE GONNA HAVE TO LEAVE SOME OF THOSE CLOTHES HOME!"

"CAN WE STICK AROUND 'TIL DARK, DAD? I WANNA SEE 'EM ROLL UP THE SIDEWALKS!"

"DOES GOD KNOW HE LEFT THE WATER RUNNING?"

"I DON'T KNOW HOW OLD MY MOM IS, BUT MY DAD IS IN THE MIDDLE AGES."

"BOY! SHE SURE HAS A LOT OF SKIN, HUH, DAD?"

"LOOK! AN AIRPLANE WITH THE PRICE TAG STILL ON IT!"

"IF I CATCH A WHALE, WILL YOU HELP ME CLEAN IT?"

"I FOUND IT LAYIN' ON TABLES IN ALL THEM REST'RANTS WE ATE AT."

"DADDY, IF WE GIVE HIM THE MONEY NOW, DO YOU S'POSE HE'LL LET US GO HOME?"

"WELL, AMEN TILL NEXT WEEK, REV'REND POLITZER."

"...AND AS I FINISHED READING 'ASK AND THOU SHALT RECEIVE', THE MITCHELL LAD YELLS: 'I WANNA ROOT BEER!'"

"I GOT TWO DIMES. HOW MUCH DID YOU GET?"

"YOU REALLY MUSTA SCARED MY DAD
THIS MORNING...HE GAVE FIVE DOLLARS!"

"BUT HE'S BAWLIN' SOMEBODY OUT...
AN' I DON'T THINK IT'S ME!"

"WHY DO THEY KEEP HARPING ON THAT
'SUFFER LITTLE CHILDREN' STUFF?"

Dennis and his dad go CAMPING

"PROMISE YOU WON'T COOK ANY OF MY FAVORITE STUFF WHILE WE'RE GONE?"

"DID YOU KNOW THAT DENNIS AND HIS FATHER LEFT FOR A CAMPING VACATION THIS MORNING?"

"THE WAY YOU YELLED, HE PROLLY WON'T *NEVER* COME BACK! HE WAS JUST LICKIN' YOUR FACE TO BE *FRIENDLY*!"

"YOU *CAN'T* USE HIM FOR BAIT NOW... HE THINKS WE'RE HIS *FRIENDS*!"

"I DON'T CARE *WHAT* MR. WILSON TELLS YOU... I'M TELLING YOU *NOT* TO GET LOST!"

"*BOY!* FIVE DAYS WITHOUT A *BATH!* THAT'S *LIVIN'*!"

"IF I KNEW A *BAD WORD*, I'D *SAY* IT!"

"WE'RE LIVIN' OFF THE COUNTRY, JUST LIKE THE *PIONEERS!*"

"BOY! YA JUST CAN'T BEAT THIS HIKIN' THROUGH THE WOODS, HUH, DAD?"

"IT'S PRETTY GOOD... CONSIDERIN'."

"WHEN ARE WE GOIN' HOME?"

"REMEMBER WHEN IT WAS RAININ' AND RUFF'S HOUSE WAS *LEAKIN'*... AN' YOU SAID FIND SOMETHIN' IN THE GARAGE TO COVER IT? WELL..."

"I BET *DANIEL BOONE* ALWAYS CARRIED EXTRA BATTERIES."

"IS *THAT* ALL YA GOT TO SAY... I NEED A BATH?"

"YOU *BOTH* NEED A BATH!"

"WE NEVER *DID* FIND OUT WHAT WAS SNORIN' IN THE BUSHES ... THAT'S WHEN WE CAME HOME."

"MAYBE NEXT YEAR I CAN CAMP OUT WITH DAD AN' *EAT AT HOME* WITH *YOU!*"

"To us they're just birds, but to Hotdog they're tiny little drumsticks."

"Don't worry, Joey...we may be lost but we're makin' good time!"

"Look, Joey! God's got his **Colorin' Set** out!"

"It's a new moon. I don't know *what* they do with their old ones."

"BUTTERFLIES MAKE IT LOOK WINDY
OUT EVEN WHEN IT ISN'T."

"WHEN A PHONE RINGS, IT TICKLES THEIR FEET.
THAT'S WHY THEY FLY AWAY."

"ALL I KNOW ABOUT THE BIRDS 'N' THE BEES IS...
SOME SING 'N' SOME STING."

"I LIKE THESE WINDY DAYS WHEN YOU CAN SEE
FUNNY STUFF THEY CAN'T BLAME YOU FOR!"

"THINKING IS WHEN YOUR MOUTH STAYS SHUT AND YOUR HEAD KEEPS TALKING TO ITSELF."

"I WONDER HOW OFTEN THEY HAVE TO CHANGE THE WATER?"

"YUP, FIVE YEARS OLD IS A VERY GOOD AGE FOR BOYS."

"BEIN' A BIG SHOT AROUND HERE IS EASY, JOEY... LONG AS THE STALE BREAD HOLDS OUT."

"SURE FISH SPEAK TO EACH OTHER, JOEY...
THEY USE *BUBBLE TALK*."

"I COULD SPEND THE REST OF MY LIFE RIGHT HERE UNDER
THIS TREE...OR AT LEAST UNTIL DINNER TIME."

"WHY DON'T WE JUST CALL UP A KID IN CHINA
AN' TELL HIM TO MEET US HALF WAY?"

"BETTER TAKE OFF YOUR SHOES...THIS
PLACE HAS SOME REALLY *GREAT* MUD!"

"SOMETHIN' FELL DOWN, JOEY! I THINK THAT'S A STRIKE!"

"THEY MUSTA BEEN PLAYIN' WITH FIRECRACKERS!'

"THAT GUY'S NAME IS JOHNNY CARSON. HE TELLS BEDTIME STORIES TO GROWN-UPS."

"IT SOUNDS TERRIBLE, JOEY, BUT I THINK IF YOUR BIRTH CERTIFICATE'S LOST, YA HAVE TO BE BORN AGAIN."

"FIREMEN USE DOGS TO HELP 'EM FIND FIREPLUGS."

"I DON'T KNOW WHETHER TO BE A CARTOONIST WHEN I GROW UP, OR WORK FOR A LIVING."

"A BOOK IS LIKE TV, ONLY YOU HAVE TO THINK UP THE PICTURE IN YOUR HEAD."

"IT'S JUST LIKE RIDIN' IN A CAR. ONLY HIGHER, AN' THEY GOT A WHOLE BUNCH O' BATHROOMS."

"MISS SITTON, WHO MADE THE LOUDEST CHALK SQUEAK... ME OR DEWEY?"

"I DON'T EVER WANT TO BE PROMOTED UNLESS YOU'RE PROMOTED, TOO!"

"WHAT DID I LEARN TODAY, MIZ BOONE? MY DAD ALWAYS ASKS ME."

"...AND TO THE REPUBLIC FOR... ..WHO'S *RICHARD STANZ*?"

"WHAT COMES BEFORE 6?" "THE GARBAGE MAN."

"IT SOUNDS KINDA LIKE BEIN' ON THE SCHOOL BUS."

"YES, IT LOOKS EXACTLY LIKE A LITTLE NAKED BOY.
NOW DRAW SOMETHING ELSE!"

"THAT'S PRETTY GOOD! YOU CAN'T EVEN SEE THE NUMBERS."

"HAVE WE PASSED THE TIME OF DAY YET?"

"ONCE IN AWHILE GOD GETS TIRED OF THINKIN' UP NEW FACES, JOEY...SO HE MAKES **TWINS**!"

"AREN'T YOU ALLOWED TO DRIVE A CAR EITHER?"

"NAW, I DON'T WANNA MEET YOUR SISTER... THERE'S TOO MANY WIMMEN IN MY LIFE *NOW!*"

"YEAH? WELL, I'VE DRANK **LOTS** OF COUGH MEDICINE, BUT IT NEVER MADE **ME** FEEL LIKE SINGIN'!"

"BEIN' ABLE TO READ JUST SPOILS A LOT OF FUN!"

"HELLO, OPERATOR ... HAVE YA GOT SOMEBODY THERE WHO CAN READ ME TO SLEEP ?"

"MOM WAS GIVIN' ME A BATH AN' SHE FELL IN !"

"MOM, WHICH HALF OF ME IS IRISH ?"

"PLEASE, GOD...BLESS AMERICA... AND MR. WILSON SAYS YOU'D BETTER HURRY."

"SORRY. GUESS I GOT THE WRONG NUMBER ...
BUT LET'S TALK ANYHOW."

"DON'T YA THINK WE OUGHTA GIVE THIS OL' TUB A *REST*?"

"CAN YOU CHEER ME UP, DAD? I THINK
I GOT THE BLUES IN THE NIGHT."

"WERE YOU PRETTY WHEN YOU WERE A LITTLE GIRL, OR
DID YOU JUST GET THAT WAY WHEN YOU GOT OLD?"

"NAW, MUSTA BEEN SOME **OTHER** ONE. THIS GUY DON'T SEEM TO *REMEMBER* US!"

"THAT'S FUNNY... MY DAD CAN TELL IF IT'S A BOY OR A GIRL JUST BY LOOKIN' AT THE BOTTOM OF ITS FEET."

"BOY, GOLDFISH DON'T GET MUCH OF A FUNERAL, DO THEY?"

"WE DON'T ACCEPT CREDIT CARDS FROM CHILDREN. BESIDES, THIS IS NOT A CREDIT CARD... IT'S A *CALENDAR* !"

THE 1980s

" WHERE DID BIRDS SIT BEFORE THERE WERE TELEPHONE WIRES ? "

"IS IT WAVIN' ITS ARMS OR SHAKIN' ITS LEGS ?"

"MOM, CAN WE HAVE HAMBURGERS FOR THANKSGIVING THIS YEAR ?"

"DO YOU THINK THERE'S A *CONNECTION* BETWEEN ALL THE BREAD WE'VE BEEN MISSING AND ALL THE PIGEONS THAT KEEP HANGING AROUND HERE ?"